TRIAGE

Leonard C. Lewin

THE DIAL PRESS
NEW YORK • 1972

Library of Congress Cataloging in Publication Data

Lewin, Leonard C
    Triage.

    I. Title.
PZ4.L6712Tr [PS3562.E928] 813'.5'4 79–38901

PRINTED IN THE UNITED STATES OF AMERICA

FIRST PRINTING

. . . Who is to be the judge of this sort of necessity? By what measure is the comparative value of lives to be measured? Is it strength, or intellect, or what? It is plain that the principle leaves to him who is to profit by it to determine. . . .

> —From the verdict of the court in *The Queen v. Dudley and Stephens,* Dec. 9, 1884, as rendered by Lord Coleridge, C.J. The case involved cannibalism among the survivors of a shipwreck.

PART ONE

CHAPTER ONE

1

New York, Jan. 2—Samuel Willis, a retired banker, died suddenly at his home here late yesterday, apparently of a heart attack. He was 83 years old.

Mr. Willis, who was widely known for his philanthropic activities, had had a long and distinguished career in finance. Eight years ago he retired as chairman and chief executive officer of the Central National Bank of New York, where he had served in many capacities since 1923. During World War II he acted as vice-chairman, later chairman, of the President's Economic Stabilization Committee, and subsequently served as an economic consultant to Presidents Truman, Eisenhower, Kennedy, and Johnson.

Since his retirement, Mr. Willis devoted most of his time to the affairs of Delphi College, which honored him last June in a special ceremony as its "most distinguished alumnus." He had been a member of the college's board of trustees since 1946, and its chairman since 1950.

Mr. Willis's celebrated collection of 17th and 18th century colonial books, paintings, and artifacts, housed in a compound near Delphi, was the destination of hundreds of visiting scholars every year. The result of his lifelong interest in pre-revolutionary Americana, the collection is considered the most representative and perhaps the most valuable of its kind in private hands.

3

Mr. Willis had been married to the former Anne Dickinson, who died last year. He leaves no immediate survivors.

2

—I'm just as surprised as you are. I thought he was in perfect health.

—So did I. But obviously there's no such thing as perfect health when you're eighty-three.

—You know, he just had his annual check-up last month. At the student health center! Everything was A–1, he told me. He was quite vain about it, to tell the truth.

—I would be too if I were his age. Well, so much for check-ups.

—Incidentally, where does that leave *us?* Do we get the estate or no? Everybody seems to have been taking it for granted, but I notice he hadn't come through with anything for a long time, unless McChesney's been holding out on us. I heard some scuttlebutt he was making things difficult. Do you know anything?

—Oh, I'm sure we'll get it. Who else would he leave it to? Mac told me months ago that they were working out the tax arrangements so that the big collection wouldn't have to be broken up. And you know Willis. If he told Mac he was "working" on something, it meant it was as good as done, or he wouldn't have mentioned it in the first place. He didn't fool around, I'll say that for him.

—Amen! I'm sorry he's dead, but it will be a relief not to have him breathing down our necks. Just the same, he could have changed his mind, you know. And it seems to me McChesney has been looking more harassed than usual lately.

—There could be a dozen other reasons for that. Don't worry, we'll get it, I'm certain, or Mac would have said something to me. I'll talk to him when he gets back from New York.

4

3

—I think we were just in time, Mr. Smith. You wouldn't believe the new conditions he was demanding for leaving us the estate. He wanted us to commit ourselves contractually to an admissions policy and a social-science teaching policy that would keep Delphi just as it was when he was an undergraduate. No "hippies," no "communism"—it would have had us tied up in court for years. And that's not all. It seems he wasn't joking when he said "it would be nice" if we changed our name to Willis University. We could have lived with *that*—for six million plus the collection—but at the rate he was going next week he might have wanted an equestrian statue of himself set up at every entrance to the campus. Plus who knows what else, and more serious. We would have become the laughing stock of the conference.

—But I do believe it, Dr. McChesney. Remember, I've heard some tapes from his lawyers' office that you don't even know about. It was worse than you think.

—Ah, yes, of course. I had forgotten how thorough your people are.

—I agree that we were just barely in time, in respect to keeping him from amending his will with impossibly restrictive conditions. But your main problem, let me remind you, was not that. In your present condition, if he had lived on only another two years, giving you only nickels and dimes on the same screwball terms, you would have lost the best of your faculty, what's left of them, and conceivably even your accreditation, if you survived at all.

—We were at his mercy, Mr. Smith. His attachment to Delphi was genuine, but he had got to the point where he had convinced himself that if we didn't do precisely what he had in mind we didn't *deserve* to survive. . . . Well, where do we go from here? What's the procedure on payment?

—It won't be difficult at all, Dr. McChesney. Complicated, perhaps, but not difficult.

5

—I hope not. As president, I normally have quite a bit of flexibility on special-purpose expenditures. It was a condition of my coming here, as I may have told you. But in our present situation my hands are tied until some of the estate funds are released. You know what small-college trustees are like, in general. A bunch of retired bigwigs, put out to pasture, who have nothing better to do with their time than prove they know how to keep books.

—Especially Willis, I would guess.

—Especially Willis. But I assure you, that had nothing to do with the, uh, question at hand.

—I know that, Dr. McChesney. We would not have undertaken the commission if it had.

—I hope what I have to do is, well, legal?

—Your concern for legality touches me, sir.

—I didn't mean——

—It's all right, Dr. McChesney, don't apologize. I couldn't resist putting your question in perspective. At any rate, the worst you will have to do is tell a few small lies that no one can refute. No one living, that is. The bill will be to the estate, not to any of your special funds, unless we have trouble with the executor. To avoid this, we may need you for corroboration.

—For instance?

—I have contracts for the sums we quoted to you, Dr. McChesney, that have Mr. Willis's signature on them. They were for services to be performed by us. Specifically, for appraisals and advice, on his collections and their management, and on the disposition of his historic real estate. We also have his written acknowledgment that the services were performed, and to his satisfaction.

—I find that hard to understand. The last thing in the world I would have expected would be for Willis to have contracted for advice about *anything*.

—You misunderstand me, sir. I didn't tell you he contracted for these services. I told you only that we have his *signature* on such contracts and on such acceptances of work performed. *Our* signa-

6

ture, of one of our organization names, is under a detailed report to Willis. Our recommendations, incidentally, will amuse you. One of them is that he insist on controlling the conditions of use of anything he turns over to Delphi.

—Let's get to the bottom of this right now, Mr. Smith. Is this the beginning of a life of blackmail for me?

—I will let the offensive implications of your remark pass, Dr. McChesney, since you are still distraught. So I will answer the question as if it were a serious one. No, it is not. Relax. Your job will be merely to testify, comment, or otherwise confirm that Mr. Willis had *mentioned* to you that he was having some work done for him by, you think, some outfit called "Special Services," or something like that. You know that it had to do with the evaluation and management of his collections—you know that he'd had appraisals made before, but you assumed he wanted them updated—but that's all you know. Nor did you ever see a copy of our report. The original, needless to say, will never be found, and our copy will not be submitted unless we are forced to produce it by court order. This should not be necessary, the substance of such reports being assumed to be of a confidential nature, if your informal remarks—and sworn testimony only if unavoidable—are sufficient, as they should be, to establish corroboration over and above a notarized contract that Willis did indeed order such a service. Do I make myself clear?

4

—Is Mr. Hermanson free?

—Here I am, Smith. Come on in. . . . Any problems?

—No. His reaction was median. But I think his period-of-fear crisis will come sooner and last a bit longer.

—You plan to keep with him yourself until he's clear? Or can we put a junior on it?

—I think I should stay with him at first, Fred. But I really would like to get on a more ambitious case as soon as I can. No difficulty in the termination, was there?

—None at all, according to Riley. He handled it. Also, the final appraisal and report are finished, Burnshaw tells me. He wants you and Riley to look it over before he closes it out.

—Fine. I'll do it now. Is the residue sheet ready?

—Yes. You can pick it up on the way out. There's practically nothing you need to remember. If we hadn't made a contingency-residue sheet an absolute rule I would have been tempted to skip one for Willis. Very, very clean. And nice work from you, too, I should say.

—Thanks, Fred. I'll see you tomorrow?

5

—Mr. Smith!

—I apologize for dropping in on you without calling first, Dr. McChesney, but I was walking past your hotel——

—Quite all right. Come in. No trouble, I hope?

—None at all. Just an informal social call, mostly. I realized after I left you this afternoon that my manner may have put you off, and I wanted to put things right if I could. I also thought we might discuss the timing of the announcement of the Willis bequest. Mostly, though, I wanted to reassure you that there would be no problems, since you were somewhat tense, I thought.

—Tense? I'm as relaxed as anyone could be, under the circumstances.

—Of course. But the circumstances are not part of your normal experience, and we have found that some of our clients occasionally develop misgivings after the fact, so to speak. Also, I thought I should explain about our report to Willis, since you were disturbed when I mentioned his holding on to the strings. I was overstating—a rather thoughtless joke. Actually, the report merely recommends that *if* he wants to limit the use of any gift he makes to Delphi, or to anyone else, he include with the gift a certain simple restriction form to ensure enforcement of his wishes.

—What was the point of it?

—We don't do anything in half-measures, Dr. McChesney. This is the kind of conservative advice any responsible consulting firm would give to a man in Willis's position who wanted assurance that he could sustain his influence with his beneficiaries. If it turns out that our document has to be produced in court at some future date it will add to its plausibility. It's a thorough and competent report. It's rather a waste that no one is likely to see it.

—Well, I'd like to see it.

—I'm sorry, Dr. McChesney, but that's against our policy. At some point you will have to testify, formally or otherwise, that you knew Willis had ordered and received it, but also that you hadn't seen it. There is no sense in exposing you to the danger of seeming to conceal something if by chance it should slip out that a copy of it was in your hands. A year or two from now, perhaps, it may be safe if you're still interested.

—I see. I think I will be. Since the collections will be in our hands, I'd welcome your advice on handling them, even though our aims are different from Willis's.

—I know. But right now such advice would be a distraction, and possibly dangerous. It's a good report, but I doubt very much that there's anything in it that you, especially, wouldn't think of. You are an unusually imaginative administrator, Dr. McChesney.

—Thank you.

—Not at all. If you weren't, I wouldn't be here, would I?

—I suppose not, if you put it that way, Mr. Smith. You said you wanted to discuss the timing of the bequest announcement?

—Oh, yes. Actually, it's not critical, since it was generally assumed by all who knew him that Willis was leaving everything to the college. But I would suggest two things. First, make no formal statement, from Delphi, until after the probate notice. Second, avoid discussion of the expected bequest as much as you can under

9

the circumstances, and do not discuss your ideas about how you will handle it until much later. And try to discourage the trustees and your faculty from such discussion. One exception: once the bequest has been officially announced, you may have to use that information as a kind of informal collateral for working funds.

—You are being unnecessarily cautious with me, Mr. Smith. I would never have considered making any kind of comment until everything was official.

—I would have been surprised if you had, but you'll forgive me again for expressing our policy of taking nothing for granted.

—Well. If that was all, Mr. Smith, perhaps you would be kind enough to satisfy my curiosity on one point, if you don't consider it too personal. How did you come to join up with Special Services? Please don't misunderstand. I have enormous respect for what you're doing. But it has struck me as odd that you're not more, well——

—More bloodthirsty? More like a Mafia killer? More sinister?

—Well, I wouldn't use those words, Mr. Smith, but that's the rough idea.

—And perhaps you also mean you wouldn't expect someone in my line of work to be so ordinary? Fair enough. I'm not offended, it's a question we've all heard before. No, I'm sorry I can't tell you anything personal about myself or my colleagues.

—I should have put it differently. I only meant to ask about how and why your group came into being, about your motivation, and so on. In general terms, not personally. You're doing something most of us don't even talk about . . . can't *bring* ourselves to talk about . . .

—Well. . . . Very well. We got together a few years ago, through a combination of circumstances and like-mindedness. Our common ground, I would say, was special training in objective analysis, plus a contempt for institutional hypocrisy. However, what gave us the impetus to organize into a *group* was the Vietnam war. We were all involved in it, each in his own way. Most of us were

10

working in military planning projects, the so-called think-tanks. Some of us were in the field. A few were merely concerned citizens, you might say. What Vietnam brought home to us most clearly was the most egregious social hypocrisy of all—the presumed sanctity of human life, which our society claims to honor. This was the alleged prime value, from which other accepted social values presumably derived. What made the mass killings in Vietnam seem especially preposterous was that they were being committed by a society claiming a greater adherence to this moral value than is claimed by any other.

People express horror at gratuitous brutality, at torture, at the Nazi death camps, at the routine outrages of any war you can think of. But it was clear to us, pragmatically, that this is hypocrisy, *socially* speaking. If mankind in general—the so-called civilized societies in particular—*truly* deplored the taking of human life it would not engage in it.

—You mean that the Vietnam atrocities made you cynical.

—No, not at all. Certainly some of us were shocked at first, and most of us came to be very much against the war, but some of us considered the killing politically necessary to the end. Eventually we all became *morally neutral*. I would not say cynical. I would say that we became as truly *objective* about the war as we had trained ourselves to be about other problems we had to deal with professionally. We came to the conclusion—oversimplifying again, of course—that, socially speaking, man was a killer of his own kind, that all pious assumptions to the contrary were fraudulent, and that whoever recognized this and acted on it would have an enormous advantage in dealing with the world as it really is. I am not, understand, pushing some banal theory of man's innate aggressiveness, or the like. I'm speaking only of man's social institutions.

—You recognize no valid morality, then.

—On the contrary! Our own personal moral values are actually quite conventional. But that's irrelevant. Our point is that many of

11

the *declared* social values that men assure each other they share are con games. They tell each other, for instance, that the preservation of someone else's life is more important to them than their own desire for money, fame, or what have you. Sometimes, perhaps, but in general, and almost always when the life in question is that of a stranger, it simply isn't. We pretend it is: that's part of the general social contract, the understanding we have with each other that enables us to go about our business unarmed, so to speak. To live and work more efficiently. It's an enormously useful convention. But it's based on hypocrisy.

—Don't we set up legal systems to protect us from each other?

—Of course. But without the general acceptance of the hypocrisy I spoke of, the law would be no real deterrent. But this is taking us afield, into dreary sociology. What I am saying, Dr. McChesney, is that our group considers all *institutional* morality, as distinguished from our own individual values, to be nonexistent. It follows that we recognize no legitimate inhibition about killing, robbing, or violating any other clause in the social contract to achieve our objectives. But we have to live with ourselves. So we limit what we do by our own code of *personal* morality. You know what I'm talking about, because you were exposed to it almost beyond your endurance before we accepted your commission. We have to be wholly convinced—by our *own* standards, such as they are—that what we do will contribute to the general human welfare, as we see it. . . . That's about as much as I can tell you, at least at this time. I hope you found it responsive, as far as it went.

• YES, the killing of Willis will go undetected. The college will stay in business, as planned. The "general welfare," as posited by Smith and McChesney, will presumably be advanced. Nobody will break down, nobody will raise difficult questions, and that will be that.

How Smith, Hermanson, and the others at the think-tank-turned-kill-tank operate varies with their projects. The details are not important and are usually not even interesting. It should be evident that a group like theirs can function successfully, given sufficient boldness, intelligence, conviction, equanimity, information, and capital. They lack none of these. A more pertinent question is how and why they can be accepted, essentially on their own say-so, by clients they couldn't conceivably have approached only a few years ago. Perhaps this will become clearer.

Another group of questions centers around Smith's "philosophical" rationale, his sanctimonious "explanation" to McChesney. Is it on the level—at least, does he believe it himself? If so, what are his deeper motives? Although he and his "Special Services" are not the subject of this book, they will appear again from time to time. So will these notes, comments, and questions.

CHAPTER TWO

1

—How many vacant beds have we got today, Winston?

—Four.

—That makes exactly forty we've promoted this month, besides those who left on their own schedules, doesn't it?

—Yes. Not bad, is it?

—No, not bad at all. Anybody getting suspicious, do you think?

—I have no reason to think so. And I don't think anybody will, if we don't push too fast. Statistically, you know, our terminals are up only about 60 per cent.

—That's quite a jump.

—Sure, Sam. But it's not too far away from normal monthly variations. And the whole point is, pretty soon the terminals will start going down and keep going down.

—When, do you figure? Statistically, I mean, when do you think they'll get down to the old normal?

—About four or five months, for a guess. Now that's assuming, of course, that we're able to improve the quality of our new admissions as much as we expect.

—Not bad, not bad at all.

2

—Dr. Post, is it my imagination, or are we losing more of the older patients than we used to? The last few weeks, I mean.

—Well, I don't know, Helen, I hadn't thought about it. You could check the figures easily enough, I think. It could be.

—Oh, I wouldn't do that. You probably think I'm a worrier for asking the question.

—Don't be silly, Helen. It may very well be. But even if it is, what would it mean? We have our ups and downs, or I guess you could say ins and outs. There's no *normal* rate. . . . Incidentally, how's the sarcoma in 21B doing today? Still in pain?

—Yes, he is, doctor, but a little better than he was yesterday.

—Well, I think we can raise his morphine dosage. No reason why he should have to put up with any more discomfort than he has to for what life he has left, poor old bastard.

—He's getting an awful lot already, doctor.

—I know. But if a little more can make it bearable for him, what's the difference? I'll put it on his chart.

—Dr. Post, does the little boy in 4B have any chance at all?

—It depends what you mean by chance, Helen. If you mean just continuing to breathe—yes, he does, at least for a few months. If you mean having any kind of meaningful life—no, not a chance. There's just not enough left of his brain and central nervous system. Considering what happened to him, it's astonishing he even made it to the hospital.

—I can't help thinking it might have been better if he hadn't.

—Of course. His parents thought they were lucky to get him in here so fast. They weren't. If they had had the usual thirty to forty minute delay that's par for emergency ambulance service in this miserable city they would have been better off.

—But they wouldn't have known it. They would have thought a faster ambulance would have saved him.

—Probably. I think I'll look in on him now.

15

3

—Sam, I just don't understand it. What the hell is Winston saving those empty beds for?

—I don't know. Why do you ask? I assume he has the usual reasons.

—Sam, the only legitimate usual reason is reserve for emergencies. I don't know exactly how many beds are supposed to be kept on hand, but it sure as hell isn't as many as I've been looking at every day this week. I have three chronics who've been waiting more than a week to get in, and those empty beds keep bugging me.

—John, I don't know the answer about those beds, but I can guess part of it. Winston is trying to cut down on the admission of chronics, who tie up bed space for months on end, as much as he can. Too many of them, more than ever, are being dumped on us by relatives who could take care of them themselves but just don't want to. I know that Winston wants to use whatever flexibility he's allowed to get more turnover for patients who need us for more than a nursing home.

—Sure, Sam, but what's new about that? I'm not proposing to fill the beds with chronics while emergencies are dying in the street outside. Any reason I have for bringing my patients in here, chronic or whatever, is not for Winston to pass judgment on. He's an administrator, and the only flexibility he has on bed assignments is to decide what a reasonable emergency reserve is. I don't have to count the empties to tell you that his recent judgment on this score leaves something to be desired.

—That may be, John, but I wouldn't be so quick to jump to conclusions. You and I don't know what the staff situation for next week looks like, for instance, and you know his attitude on admissions we can't properly handle. I agree with him completely on this. The fact is, we all have to make our decisions every day about who needs our time more than the next man. And I'll tell you this, John, what bugs *me* a lot more than having some of my chronics have to wait too long to get beds is having to look every day at the filled beds and be reminded of all the waste of our facilities on chronics who don't need to be here.

—What would you do with them, Sam? You talk about nursing homes, but most of these chronics don't have that alternative. Or any other, often.

—Take a tougher line on admissions, if I had authority to set standards. *Force* the people responsible for chronics and terminals we can't help to look elsewhere to care for them. And when they can't, force the state or the city or the federal government to recognize *their* responsibilities. They'll never get around to looking at the facts of terminal illness for what they are until they're forced to. They will have to decide, sooner or later, just what they're willing to spend, or should be willing to spend, on people who are near the end. And they have to be *forced* to stop confusing the practice of therapeutic medicine with care for the moribund, at the expense of patients who *can* be saved. We lose too damned many for this reason alone, who could have made it if we weren't overloaded with hopeless cases.

—You haven't said it, Sam, in so many words. But you implied that some government agency should set dollar equivalents on extending life. Like up to thirty dollars a day, and no more, or up to three months' nursing, and no more. You don't mean that, I hope.

—Why not? John, we do it anyway, and we'll continue to set some kind of quota on the dying, how far we'll go with them, as long as we recognize any obligation at all to maintain their lives —and as long as we can't or won't assign the funds and personnel to meet the demands of all who need this kind of care or want it. Why shouldn't we candidly recognize what we're doing, and act accordingly? Instead of proceeding on a hit or miss basis, with priorities left entirely to chance.

—What you're saying, Sam, is that we all have to play God to a certain degree anyway, so why not be businesslike about it. It sounds good, but I don't buy it. I don't think it's just a matter of degree and procedures. A crisis is one thing, when you have to abandon one patient to save another, but there's no crisis here. When it comes to fighting for public money to set up facilities for chronics and terminals, I'll go with you all the way, but I'm not going to foreclose on any of my patients until I have to. And if this is what Winston is up to, I'll fight him on it too.

4

—We're in for some trouble, Winston. Helen O'Connor, on the fourth floor, is beginning to wonder about the termination rate. And John Neustadt started to blow off this morning about the empty beds. He told me he's going to fight you on it if he doesn't get a satisfactory answer.

—Well, we expected it. Did you sound him out for a reaction?

—Yes, and it was negative. He'll ask questions at the next staff meeting. You'll have to anticipate him by announcing the new reserve policy. And I'll see that we have enough legitimate emergencies in the beds before then to prove your case.

—Think we're ready to take a strong line?

—Yes. Actually, I don't think we'll have any choice, but it's just as well. You'll have the statistics ready, I assume.

—Of course. Are you going to hold back on terminations until then?

—No. But I plan to take care of only three. And I'll try to bring in most of the emergencies on the same day, as if on a wave. It should help. Twenty-one B should be through some time tonight, 4B and 8A over the weekend. I'll have at least six, maybe as many as nine, new cases in on Friday. One way or another, we'll be full by the Monday meeting. Timing sound right to you?

—Perfect. We'll have a real hospital here yet, by God.

5

—Nettie, there's no reason for you to take on so. You know you did all you could for your father, and so did the doctors.

—I know, I know. But I still feel as if it's my fault somehow. Because there were times when I *wished* it was all over.

—That's not so terrible, Nettie. You heard what the doctor said. If your father lived on another week, or a month or two, he would have either been in misery all the time or so doped up he couldn't think or know what was going on. What would have been the point?

—Oh, I know what the doctor said! But how does he know what my father was thinking? How does he know he didn't want to live, no matter how much pain? Just because he couldn't talk. I can't help thinking he would have lasted a lot longer if they hadn't doped him so much. And that he would have wanted to. Nobody asked *him*.

—Nettie, you're talking nonsense. You know they did all they could to save him. You're taking it out on them because you feel guilty. Because *you* really wanted it to be over. And so did I. And why shouldn't we, for God's sake? What's wrong with it? Never mind what your father *might* have wanted. Would *you* really have wanted another three months of this?

• ANYONE who thinks Dr. Sam Post and administrator Winston are heading for trouble because their methods of weeding out the hopeless cases from the hospital roster are so crude is wrong. No one will accept, whatever the passing suspicion, the outrageous notion that they are doing exactly what they are doing. This is the great tactical advantage of boldness, and they know it as well as any professional criminal, athletic coach, or demagogue. Dr. Neustadt will complain about the reserve policy, but nothing will come of it. They are well ahead of him.

Any "explanation" of Dr. Post's psychological motivation would be supererogatory to this story. He has been in the business of making life and death judgments all his professional life anyway. Deciding to destroy a life is not very different from deciding to fight to save one—in scale or in style or in mood. And he always knows just *whom* he is "terminating"; he cannot insulate himself with a comfortable cushion of abstraction, as do those who make such judgments on a statistical basis to implement a policy.

CHAPTER THREE

1

New York, Jan. 19—Over six hundred drug addicts died here last month, according to a report released today by the Medical Examiner's office. In a statement issued by Dr. Spiro White, an associate medical examiner, it was revealed that the record death count was five times that of the previous December. Most of the new victims were teenagers.

"The reason for the excessive death rate is not yet clear," said Dr. White. "We have no basis for believing that the use of 'hard' drugs is appreciably greater than it has been, nor have we found any evidence of poisonous adulteration of the prevailing supplies of heroin." Most drug addicts here are users of heroin.

Dr. White suggested that those who died may have been, ironically, the victims of a temporary improvement in the quality—and therefore in the concentration and lethal effectiveness—of current supplies of the drug. "An addict who is accustomed to using an adulterated heroin containing perhaps 90 per cent of neutral filler will be trebling his dose if he switches to a heroin containing only 70 per cent filler," he pointed out. "In the cases of the many addicts who have been ingesting heroin at a level already approaching their tolerance for the drug, such a difference could well be fatal."

Also mentioned in the report is a possible synergistic effect of high air pollution levels on heroin absorption. Last month

21

new high-concentration records were set for several of the more common air pollutants, including carbon monoxide, sulphur dioxide, and benzpyrene.

2

—What we wanted to talk to you about, Dr. White, was this story in the paper about this new high-grade heroin that's killing off the junkies.

—Certainly, Inspector. If I can be of help, I'd——

—We'll get right to the point, Dr. White. We want to know what makes you think the heroin going around the trade last month was that much better than the month before.

—Well, it was just conjecture, of course, as I thought my statement made clear. There has to be some explanation for what's been happening. Statistically, you know, it couldn't possibly be merely an abnormal random variation. It seemed to me to be the most likely, or, better, least unlikely, of the possible reasons anyone in this office could come up with.

—We have news for you, Doc. The stuff they got last month was the same stuff they been getting all along. No better, no worse.

—Are you sure of this?

—Positive. In New York, you got only three main sources it comes in from. We get samples from all of them, almost every day. They go into territories, very tight control. Nobody fools around.

—You mean whatever killed these addicts couldn't have come from another source?

—It's possible, but I wouldn't believe it. These junkies you say took ODs without knowing it, they were from all over the city. If they got stuff from someplace else we don't know about yet, it means there wasn't just one or two, but maybe forty or fifty pushers out ready to take some real big chances with the mob. It don't figure.

—I see. What ideas do your people have on it?

—Right now, we don't. First we thought it had to be ODs, what else? But we don't hear a whisper about any new round of shooting high. What about this air pollution thing? Is that serious?

—Well, yes and no. We don't really know if there's a connection, it's just another guess. But it could only be a factor along *with* an overdose, we think, so it's no answer. I suppose if there were anything poisonous in the trade heroin you would have found it. We didn't catch anything traceable in autopsies.

—Which leaves us nowhere, which is where we came in. Lieutenant McBride here has all his inside people trying to track it down, but so far we have nothing. But let me give you a little advice. If you get any new ideas, let me know about it so we can talk it over before you go to the papers with it. O.K.?

—I understand. . . . I think. I'll be glad to talk over anything we come up with, of course. But as for *clearing* it with you, if that's what you mean, that's ridiculous. Why should we do that?

—Look, Dr. White, handling the junkies is our business, not yours. We know how they act when they read a junk story in the papers. You don't. This last story, you probably thought it might have scared them into cutting down, or some of them even trying to come clean, right?

—I would think so, yes.

—Let me tell you. A lot of them, maybe even most of them, did start to cut down, taking maybe half the usual. Scared of an OD, like your story said. And they like the idea that maybe the habit won't cost so much. But then they find they didn't take enough, they don't have enough on hand, and they go wild, lots of them, looking for a fix. Which means big trouble. Then you have the pushers not making out, so they start looking for new kinds of business we don't have any line on.

—I don't see what's wrong with that, if it cuts down the drug traffic.

—Sure, sure. But the main thing, for us, is keeping in control of the situation, which we can't do if things don't stay on an even keel.

We need a drug market that's *stable*. It's the only way we can keep our hand in, know what's going on, so we can keep them quiet. As long as the pushers and the users know where they stand and know that *we* know where they stand, you're not going to have the junkers breaking into your doctors' offices. Get it?

—I'm not sure that I do, Inspector Glass. It sounds as if you're telling me that you want the drug traffic kept just the way it is, but you can't mean that. Certainly you're not saying you're opposed to cutting down on drug addiction.

—Don't get wise with me, Doc. I didn't say anything like that, and you know it. When I tell you we have to keep things stable, I mean gradual. So we know what's going on. The big crime you get from junkies, what everybody talks about, the big fuss, comes when things get stirred up. It don't matter from what. When no stuff comes in—a panic—we have trouble. When too much comes in, we have trouble. When new people try to break into the business, we have trouble. When everything is like it should be, we have no trouble at all.

—Then I didn't misunderstand you at all, Inspector. You'd rather have the dope situation stay just as it is than risk trouble by shaking it up. As long as everything stays quiet.

—Let me put it to you this way, Doc. If I had a choice between letting the dope business stay the way it is or cutting it in half in a week, it would stay put. How about that? And let me tell you something else while we're on it. Having junkies around is not all bad, what do you think of that? When you have a criminal—a real pro, I mean—who's on junk, you have a handle on him. You have some control. It's not the worst thing in the world. Not from where we have to work, Doc.

3

—I'm telling you, Seymour, it was practically a confession. I think if I pushed him I could have got him to brag about how he put this crook or that pimp on drugs himself. But I didn't want to stretch my luck.

—I wish I could be as sure as you are that we're doing the right thing. Don't worry, Spiro, I'm not going to carry on again. But I can't help having this feeling that we're killing some people we shouldn't be.

—Seymour, your neurosis is perfectionism. You shouldn't have become a social worker. We've been through this time and again. Let's try the catechism once more. Did you or did you not personally supervise the distribution of all the special heroin?

—Yes, but——

—Were you, or were you not, satisfied that every user who got it was clearly warned—either by you or Vinnie or Clara—that if he used more than half his usual dose it could kill him? And that he understood what you told him?

—Yes, but I still don't know that some of it wasn't passed on without the warning.

—Seymour, you try my patience. Weren't you satisfied at any rate that the stuff went only to the real gone hopeless cases? Who wouldn't share the time of day with anybody, much less the only dope they had?

—It could have been taken from them.

—By whom? More of the same types we're getting rid of. Who else?

—There could be exceptions.

—One or two, maybe? Seymour, call it a dozen if you like. How could that stack up, in any way you can count it at all, against the lives we've *already* saved? Statistically, these vermin would have killed, between them, at least forty people—clean people, innocent people, good kids—during the next three years alone. They would have ruined the lives, what was left of them, of who knows how many more? Certainly at least one apiece. And none of this tells us how many the publicity will scare off—and save. If we can keep going a while longer we may clean up this whole rotten scene—and

25

get ready to go after another. Think about it.

—Spiro, I know you're right, and you know I know you're right. I said I wasn't going to bug you again. But I'm just not as happy about it as I thought I would be, that's all. I don't want to talk about it any more, O.K.?

—Except for one thing I have to tell you again, because you have to keep putting what we're doing in perspective, or it means nothing. Now, you're not a nut, and I'm not a nut—there isn't a nickel's worth of megalomania between us, is there? But the fact is—the *fact,* mind you—the fact is that we are doing a truly great thing! This is the perspective. We are doing a remarkable thing in behalf of the general welfare. We are not doing it for profit, and we don't expect ever to be able to take credit for it. We don't claim to be geniuses, and we don't claim to be heroes. What we see has to be done is what anyone can see—except that everyone else puts his hand over his eyes. Or else lacks just that little extra bit of courage —it doesn't take a real hero, the risk isn't that great. What we *have* done is just to have looked at the simple logic of what *has* to be done, and to have taken the extra step of acting on it. Simple. But the results are great, or will be great—why minimize it? This is the perspective. We have to keep it in mind, all the time. We are beginning what may become the complete eradication of social disease. No less.

—All *right,* Spiro!

4

—So the narco squad is putting the heat on you about me? I'm not surprised, Roger.

—Well, I guess you must have touched a sensitive spot somewhere when you talked to Glass. I don't know about what, Spiro, and I don't even want to know. All that's relevant, as I see it, is that we have to get along with other departments, especially the police. Yes. If they're unreasonably sensitive, *we* can afford to make allowances. Can't we? In the future, I'll do the talking for our office, at least to them. No criticism implied, Spiro, but you know as well as I do that you tend to be somewhat abrasive with bureaucrats you think are fools.

—Roger, if you're going to have to be our ambassador to the cops along with everything else you do, I think it's important that you know *why* Glass is sore at me. It wasn't just another case of wise-guy Doctor White giving his usual lip to a stuffed shirt, I assure you. If that was it, you *should* criticize me, without being polite about it. I can take it. But that wasn't it. There's a real issue involved that concerns our whole way of operating, not just me.

—Really? The impression I had from Glass is that you were trying to needle him about not going after junkies more. I want you to know that I share your reservations about what his squad does, or doesn't do, but I see nothing to be gained by baiting him about it.

—I see you've jumped to a conclusion, Roger. I thought you said you didn't know what was involved. It's a little different. He told me, in practically so many words, that he doesn't *want* to cut down addiction unless it can be done so gradually that nobody's boat is rocked. The junkies, the pushers, the cops—especially the cops. I'm not exaggerating, Roger. It came out because of the statement I put out on the junkie death epidemic. He and his boys are more upset by that statement than they've ever been, as far back as I can remember, about junkie crime and murder. What he wanted from me, and what he didn't get, was a commitment to let him censor any statement we might want to issue that had anything to do with addiction. That's what he's sore about, and I would hope he'll get just as sore at you when you turn him down, no matter how polite you are. It isn't just me he's pissed off at.

—Well, Spiro, I did agree to consult him before we issued any more releases. I saw no harm in it. If that's all the issue was, I can't get too excited about it.

27

—No? Let me spell it out for you. What bothered him about the statement, my statement, was that it scared a lot of junkies into cutting down, a few maybe even to cutting out. As I hoped it would, naturally. But he doesn't want this, he said. It interferes with the stability of the dope trade. It makes trouble. Pushers have to look for other ways of earning a buck. This, believe it or not, is *bad,* according to Glass. They have what amounts to a comfortable live-and-let-live arrangement with the dope trade, and they don't want to spoil it. Anything that throws dope consumption out of whack means they will have new situations to cope with, which can be uncomfortable, even dangerous, and may even mean they'll have to work——

—Now, wait a minute, Spiro——

—or will be so successful in cutting down the dope trade that their guys will be forced back on to some dreary, unprofitable beats. I'm not saying Glass even thinks this way about it, necessarily, but the narco squad has as much of a vested interest in *maintaining* the dope traffic as the runners themselves, or——

—You're going too far, Spiro, much too far. You are charging them with total corruption. What you said is irresponsible, and actionable as well. I can't have this, Spiro.

—Roger, you weren't there! I'm telling you that Glass said as much himself! I don't think he realized what he was admitting. I didn't mean to suggest that he *said* his boys are on the take from the dope mobs, but it's a logical inference from what he did say. He said, flatly, that he doesn't *want* the dope traffic cut down unless it can be done slowly enough so that nobody in it gets hurt. He doesn't want us to scare off the addicts. I'm telling you, and you'll see, that any statement you draw up that could reasonably be expected to scare off borderline cases he'll tell you—ask you—to tone down. If you stand up to him, as I'm sure you will, he'll have a bigger beef than if you didn't agree to let him see the statement in the first place.

—Well, I won't debate it with you, Spiro, because, as you said,

I wasn't there. But I have to remind you that narcotics-law enforcement is his responsibility, not ours. And it's just possible that he knows his business better than we do. Let's not be presumptuous. Let's not jump to conclusions. A little humility, Spiro, a little humility! It *is* possible, you know, that your inference was wrong. Or that what he said was not exactly what he meant to say. We'll find out soon enough.

—I hope you're right. But I think it was a mistake to agree to consult him before issuing any more releases. It puts you on the spot instead of him. Either you keep compromising, a few little words here, a few words there, or you're up against the wall with him—and you don't have any loudmouth troublemaker like Doctor White to blame it on to keep the peace. There are advantages to having someone like me around, you know—it isn't all bad!

5

New York, Jan. 26—The cause of the recent increase in heroin deaths in the city remains unknown, according to Dr. Roger S. Friendly, Chief Medical Examiner. Although overdosage is clearly involved, he said in a press conference today, earlier speculation about a possible increase in purity in local heroin supplies appears unfounded.

Inspector Henry Glass, of the Police Department's Narcotics Control Squad, who participated in the conference along with Dr. Friendly, reported that samples of heroin currently available to addicts are not substantially different from other samples tested by police laboratories over the last year. Police technicians routinely check all drugs taken in hand, he said. The frequency of small drug seizures is so great, Inspector Glass explained, that any important change in the quality of illegal drugs would be known within 48 hours of its appearance in retail channels.

According to Dr. Friendly, the investigation into the causes of the abnormally high drug fatality rate will continue until further notice. A task force from the Medical Examiner's office and the Police Department has been assigned to the project.

• IT'S not difficult to kill people if one really wants to; even the special resources available to Dr. White are not that hard to come by. And killing one victim at a time is very much the same proposition that it's always been, as the political assassins keep proving. That's what Seymour and his friends have been doing to the hapless junkies, with a certain amount of guidance and technical assistance. Perhaps, for the sake of efficiency, they will develop a special technology for their project, to provide a multiplier effect, as in other modern processes. Efficient or not, they have already adopted that degree of presumption normally reserved for themselves by those who claim political authority over the lives of others.

CHAPTER FOUR

1

—In the long run the whole damned industry is expendable, Earl, and you know it as well as I do.

—Well, I wouldn't go so far as to say that, Harold. It won't be as essential as it still is, of course, but——

—But nothing. Bullshit. People still need coal—they need it only because they can get it. So today there's a big shortage on, a strip-mine boom, high prices and the rest. Because nuclear power plants haven't taken over as fast as some people thought they would. So what. Supposing the word was out that there would be no more underground coal mines operating in this country ten years from now. You think it would be so terrible?

—I don't know, Harold. But I don't think you're being realistic for right now, never mind the long run. Have you any idea what it would take for half the power plants to switch from coal? And what about steelmaking?

—Spare me the statistics, Earl. The point is that they could be converted, and in less time than you think, as long as people knew it was coming and they had to do it. Remember anthracite? But as long as they don't have to they'll drag their feet, and to hell with what happens to your people. To hell with the miners and their families. As long as business is good for the mine owners and the power companies.

—Not for all of them, Harold. What bothers me isn't the working miners. The work is better than it used to be, and they have a pretty fair contract. But it's the automation. The mines that need a lot of miners are the ones that keep closing down, one after another. Sure, the young people don't want to go into the mines, and they leave, but the industry is thinning down a lot faster than that. Problem is that the miners who get left in these old coal towns where there's nothing else to do when the mine closes, what happens to them and their families? They don't know anything else. The government people talk a lot about bringing in new industries, and they send committees, but it don't amount to anything. We have to get these people out of these towns. Enough of them, anyway, so there's enough work for those who want it. The government still won't put up the kind of money it'll take to send them someplace else, and nobody else wants them anyway, and we don't have what it takes.

—And black lung doesn't scare them out? Or the mine explosions?

—Not enough so's you'd notice. Every time there's a big one a lot of the miners say they're getting out, they've had enough, they don't want to wait till it's their turn. But then there's a big stink, a crackdown on the mine inspectors, and some new laws, and they say, well, it'll be better now maybe, and they stay on, except for a few. Point is, they don't have any choice, *that's* the problem. Then some more mines close.

—You mean they haven't been scared out *yet.*

—Never will be, neither. Eighty thousand killed since they started counting in 1910, never mind black lung. And the new safety rules haven't helped the figures any, so far as I can see. No, they'll just keep dying out the way they're doing. It's a hell of a thing, Harold. Nobody outside pays it much mind either, except when there's a big cave-in on the television. It's so gradual nobody notices.

—It doesn't have to be so gradual, Earl. Now just suppose for a minute. Suppose we have a lot of cave-ins next summer. Explosions. Fires. Gas. And big ones. All within a few months.

—But we won't, Harold, so why talk about it?

—Bear with me a little, Earl. Supposing, as I say, we had these explosions. And supposing that most of them were in mines that had good safety records. And supposing it turned out that the government had to declare a whole *class* of mines irrevocably unsafe, for some new reason nobody thought of before.

—What kind of mines you talking about?

—Hell, I don't know! Just listen. Oh, say for example that it applied to all mines that went more than so many feet underground. Or more likely, mines in certain kinds of geological formations. What's the difference? Anyway, let's say half the mines had to be closed *overnight.* If something like that happened, the government would damned well have to take care of those people then, right? I mean, *really* take care of them.

—Maybe.

—What do you mean, maybe? Think about it a little. Of course they would. And I mean the federal government, of course, not the two-bit state legislatures.

—I still mean maybe. Maybe they'd do what they did before in the mountains—build highways. A lot of jobs for a while, then it's over, and the people are worse off than they were before. And I'm not sure I like your line of talk, Harold. You sound as if you're getting ready to blow up the mines.

—I'm not getting ready to do anything. I just think I know how to solve your problem, if you're not afraid to face it the way it has to be faced. What I was supposing is the only answer, unless we get a different kind of government, or unless you're willing to wait forever while nature takes its course, while the old miners just fade away. But if you were you wouldn't have come to talk to me about it, would you?

—No. But I was hoping you might come up with something constructive.

—Maybe I have. There's someone I want you to meet who I think can be helpful. Can you make it here tomorrow about seven thirty in the evening?

2

—If I understand you right, Mr. Smith, what you figure to do is blow up a hell of a lot of mines or something so that it looks like a new kind of accident that can't be prevented.

—Not an accident, Mr. Holly. A *condition* that has reached a certain point in a very large portion of the industry and that is economically uncorrectable.

—Just how do you figure to go about it?

—The less you know about what will happen and when it happens, the better, Mr. Holly. All I will tell you is that after this series of disasters takes place, the reason for it will seem obvious to the Bureau of Mines. They will not be able to paper it over. A large percentage of mines, more than half, will have to be closed permanently, and the federal government will have to reestablish the mine communities as economically viable, whatever it may cost. Relocate them if necessary. Bring in real industries, permanent ones, subsidize them if they have to, set up real training programs to last. That's the only way they *ever* get important things done, long-range programs—when there's a real catastrophe situation. That's the way your people will get back into the main currents of American life.

—But a lot of miners will get killed.

—The fewer the better, Mr. Holly, but the operation has to be entirely credible. There will be a lot killed, Mr. Holly, I will not minimize it. What you have to decide is whether a few hundred miners dead a few years before their time is a fair price for saving the futures of a hundred thousand mine families. I have no intention of selling you on this plan, Mr. Holly. If you can solve the problem some other way, please do. Our staff has examined the situation very carefully since Mr. Peterson told us about the problem, and we have concluded that there is no other solution more than remotely possible for the foreseeable future. If you let it drift, nothing will happen. As I told you before, we would not even consider the commission otherwise. Nor would we consider it if we were not fully satisfied that our efforts would result in a clear and substantial improvement in the condition of your people—by our standards, which are more hard-headed than those of any other institution engaged in social action.

—I don't like it, Harold. And I'm not all that sure it would work out like he says.

—Damn it, Earl, you're not supposed to *like* it! The question is, are you tough enough to face up to it?

—I wish I could talk it over with a few people I know. This is no kind of thing for one man to take on by himself.

—I'm sorry, Mr. Holly, but that's the way it has to be. As I know Mr. Peterson told you, we will not do business with anyone who for any reason whatever may be tempted to discuss it with someone else. This limits us, of course, to dealing with persons like yourself who can make commitments without being accountable to others. There are not many of you. But you are the people who get things done.

—I'll have to think about it.

—Of course. We would do nothing in any case until you were so firmly convinced of the necessity of the operation that you were pushing us to go ahead.

—Harold, is there anything else I ought to know?

—What do you mean? Whatever you have in mind, ask Smith while he's here.

—Well, about arrangements, and so forth.

—They are very simple, Mr. Holly, as is true with anything big. When you decide you want to go ahead, let me know through Mr. Peterson. We will work out our plans, but all you will know will be what the costs will be, and nothing on paper. You will be told

35

of no details, except for the procedure on payment, which is different in every case we handle. When the operation is completed, you will see me once, at which time I will tell you how to proceed, if indeed there is anything to proceed with, which in this case I doubt. That's all.

—No red tape at all, Earl. I can tell you, I've dealt with Smith before. You have to make one tough decision, but that's it.

—I'll think about it. Thanks very much for coming, Mr. Smith, and for the time your people put in already.

—At your service, Mr. Holly. And one word of advice. Take your time about making up your mind. Don't even think about it at all for a week.

3

—What's your impression, Earl? Outside of the fact that the whole proposition scares you?

—I still don't like it, Harold. I tell you, I don't even rightly know if I believe it. If this Smith acted like some kind of gangster . . . well. But he's so damned businesslike and stuffy, it's creepy.

—There's nothing creepy about the way his organization works. They're absolutely straight. They're dependable, and they're honest. And they're not greedy, that really impresses me. You would think they would set their prices on what the traffic will bear—after all!—but they don't. They figure their costs, and they add on a margin that's usually a lot less than a retail store gets. They also show you where and how to get the money to pay for it. You'll probably get a bill for a very carefully justified consulting service, I imagine, and it'll be worth having just for the education. I wish everyone I did business with behaved the way they do.

—What's your arrangement with them, Harold?

—You mean do I get a commission? Not a penny. They don't

work that way, and it suits me just fine. I'll bill you for my time just as I always do, and that's it, whether you deal with them or not.

—You don't want to be a party to what they do, right?

—Right. But don't get me wrong. It's not because I don't approve of what they do, or I wouldn't have steered you to them. It's because I don't know exactly what they do, I don't want to know, and I have no control over it. I have simply introduced you to an organization I think may be the right one to solve a problem for you, that you wouldn't have known about otherwise. I've done this for you before. The only difference is that these people are willing to take on solutions that the rest of us are too hypocritical to even think about.

—But what about the risk? This guy Smith doesn't know me from a hole in the ground. How does he know for sure I won't spill everything?

—I used to wonder about that, and I asked him. He just laughed. He said they have their own ways of knowing what's safe and what isn't. Trade secret. For one thing, you know, who'd believe you? Some cock-and-bull fantasy about some mysterious guy named "Smith" whom you don't know and can't produce? I tell you, Earl, these people know exactly what they're doing. I've never said that about anyone else.

—Harold, for the ten years I know you you never steered me wrong. But this time I wonder. . . . Harold, I'm not going to go ahead on this thing. I just don't have what it takes. I'm just not all that sure.

—It's up to you. But you don't get off the hook that easily, Earl. Because now that you know that there *is* a solution to your problem, you're responsible. Whether you deal with them or whether you do nothing. You can't *un*-know it. And you know I'm right.

—Maybe. But the answer is still no, so far as I'm concerned. If somebody else hires Smith to do the same business, I won't say

37

beans about it, and more power to them, but it won't be me.

—Then it won't be anyone, Earl, you know damned well.

—Then it won't be anyone.

• SMITH again, but this time he's drawn a blank. He seems to have been overselling a pretty dubious proposition anyway. However. . . . One of the more delicate aspects of his enterprise is how he makes contact with likely clients. Obviously, he and his group have a good sense of where their institutional prospects lie. And they learn a great deal about persons like Earl Holly before they talk with them. For all Smith's casual blather about their "ways of knowing what's safe" they are far too methodical to depend on mere intuition, however sensitive, for anything so important.

Harold Peterson is one of a number of go-betweens they use; he is part of a small network of middlemen they set up when they started out. Harold is a "management" consultant and lawyer. He is an "objectivist" on the same wave length as the Smith–Hermanson group, he shares their moral arrogance, he is intelligent, bold, and honest. His reliability is more critical to the group than is that of potential clients, like Earl Holly.

But this is an operational detail. More substantive is that men like Peterson are available, and that men like Holly will at least listen.

CHAPTER FIVE

1

—Otto, it's simple arithmetic. We have only eighty thousand dollars to spend for the whole year. We can't get any more. If we do nothing at all—I mean really nothing—we can't make it through the year unless fifteen or twenty of the inmates are taken off our hands by September. And that's net, Otto—it means we don't replace any of them no matter how loud anybody hollers. Those are the hard figures. And that doesn't allow that least little bit for repairs, or for more money for the staff, or for anything except what's already there. Now when the state comes in and says we have to fireproof the carpet and the curtains, and put in two more fire escapes and two firewalls, they'll just have to do it themselves. But by law they can't do it either. We can rip out the carpets and curtains if we have to, but the fire escapes and firewalls—if you have an idea, you tell me.

—Well, suppose we ask for contributions and volunteers. Or a special surtax, if we have to. Just lay it on the line to the good folks of Cadie County. Tell them exactly what we need and why, and dump it in their laps. What do you think, Cecil? What about you, Mary?

—Otto, not only would nothing happen, but we'd get most of the folks down on us besides. Let's face it, nobody really gives a damn about the people in the county home, and nobody wants to be reminded of it. They don't care what we do or don't do just so long as they don't have to hear about it. Or pay another nickel to keep it going. Now that's the God-honest truth.

—Cecil's right, Otto. And the ones with relatives in the home will be the worst. They feel guilty about it, and they will surely blame us for the way they feel. That's psychology. The only time they'll thank us is when we leave them alone. They know what the home is like, but they don't want us to tell them. They just don't want to think about it. You can understand them, can't you?

—Well, now, damn it, I just got elected County Commissioner by promising I'd help run the county as if it was my own business, and everybody knew I meant it. Now where does that leave me, I ask you? You two have been living with this for a long time. I'm new. What the devil do we do? If the state says we have to spend money, and the voters won't give us the money to spend, where does that leave us?

—Up the creek. Simmer down, Otto, no need to get your bowels in an uproar. There's not many things we *can* do, so that makes the problem easier, is the way I see it. I don't say I like it, but there it is. Now the first thing we have to do is cover ourselves on the fire rules. Legally, we can't spend the money or kick anybody out, so far as the county's concerned, but legally we *have* to, says the state. So it seems to me that number one is we put all the facts in a letter to the Department of Health and Public Safety and publish it as a legal notice. That gets us off the spot.

—Then what?

—Then we make it our main business to cut costs. We just can't get any lower on food or staff or medical. We have to get people out.

—You mean try to talk some of the inmates into leaving? Finding some relatives to take care of them?

—Hell, no. Otto, I don't think you appreciate it yet how rotten things are in the home. We're just plain lucky we haven't had some troublemaker nosing around and writing it up. If any inmate had a prayer of any place else to go, he'd go. He'd have gone long ago, I tell you. No, what I think we have to do first is have some private talks with relatives. We know of relatives for about a third of the inmates; most of them live in the county or nearby. I think we go after them. Have them come in to talk to us *at* the home, so they can't pretend they don't know what it's like. Tell them it will get worse. I don't think we'll get more than a couple out that way, but we may be able to pick up a little money. It's worth a try. Not because we'll get much, but just to serve notice.

—It isn't worth the time, Cecil. It never worked before.

—Don't I know it, Mary. But I think we have to do it anyway. The main thing still is we have to hope a lot of inmates will pass on. And fight like hell against any new admissions, no matter what. And see what happens.

—Can't we put some of them into the county hospital?

—No help, Otto, we've done that before. The hospital charges come out of the home budget. That makes it even worse. We try to keep them *out* of the hospital if we can. Dr. Evans knows that and cooperates real well.

—I don't suppose we could get some money from a private charity? Or a church?

—No. They all tell us: The county is supposed to be taking care of these people, we have our own jobs. They're only interested in special causes. Now last year McCallum and Parker, the big drug company, gave us a real good offer. Free drugs and medicines if we let them use the inmates for some simple experiments. We took them up on it, but we had to stop. There was a big stink about it. Illegal, too, and we can't try it again. If I'd handled it right, nobody would have known, but it's too late.

—Hell's fire, Cecil, doesn't anybody give a damn about these people? If they don't, why do they bother to have a county welfare home in the first place?

—Times have changed, Otto. It used to be Cadie County people felt some responsibility for their own folks who couldn't work and had no homes. And setting up the county home was the cheapest way to take care of the most people who needed help. But nowadays everybody figures the country is so rich, all these big government programs, let somebody else worry. The fact is they don't really care, so one excuse is as good as another.

—Just like Mary says, Otto. Another thing, most people feel that the inmates don't really count. As people, you know what I mean? They don't contribute to the economy, they're just a drain, who needs them, they'd be better off dead. Now nobody ever says that right out, but that's the way they feel, and you better believe it.

—Hell's fire, Cecil, if nobody else cares about them I wonder why the devil we should.

2

—Mr. Siebert, our taxes have gone up every year now for ten years, and you don't have as many people in the home as you had ten years ago. I don't see why you should be having trouble taking care of them all of a sudden.

—It's not all of a sudden, Ben, except for the new state fire ruling I told you about. It's been getting worse every year for a long time, because the taxes don't nearly keep up with the inflation. The home has always been low man on the county budget, because nobody can see the good coming out of it. If I knew how bad it was before I was elected to the commission, I would have campaigned for more money for the home.

—Then you wouldn't have got elected, Mr. Siebert, I don't think. Meaning no disrespect. Everybody knows the people in the home are bums mostly, except maybe for the old ones. If the do-gooders in Washington are so worried about them, let them take care of them. They have the money.

—I wish they would, Ben, more than you, but it's not that simple legally. So you're not about to help out, right?

—I do help out, Mr. Siebert, and I don't see why I should help

42

any more. I pay taxes, same as everybody, and there hasn't been a year go by I don't have clothes for the collection in October. And I gave the home my old television set last year besides, and I don't remember what-all the year before. I'm not a rich man, I work for a living same as everybody, and I figure I'm doing good taking care of my own family.

—I understand, but I had to ask you. Another thing. Are there any other relatives who might take your uncle in? Or help out?

—Not a one, Mr. Siebert. My cousins out west would laugh at me if I asked. The plain truth, Mr. Siebert, is my uncle has always been a bum and the family don't feel they owe him nothing. Me neither. I figure I'm doing my share and more. If the state says you have to have fire escapes, can't the state pay for them?

3

—I don't want to say I told you so, but it sure was a waste of time, wasn't it? Not a one off our hands, not even a dime for the fund, just another pile of old clothes we have to clean and two more TVs that probably won't be worth repairing.

—You were right, Mary, but I think we had to ask. How do you feel now about what we told you before, Otto?

—I don't know what to think. I thought you were exaggerating. Like you said, nobody cares. And like Mary said, the relatives are the worst. Most of them *I* talked to were sore at *me*, as if I was the one who didn't care about their sister or their uncle or their grandma.

—Well, now, Otto, don't be too hard on them. Try to put yourself in their shoes. Why should you have to carry all this dead weight that doesn't mean beans to you and probably never did? It's one thing if you have money to spare and if you cared, but if it was like that you wouldn't have your kin going into the home in the first place, now, would you?

—Dead weight, you said. You mean they'd all be better off dead, don't deny it. Nobody'd have to think about them, nobody'd feel guilty, nobody'd be sore at us, and the county would have money in the bank for something everybody wants. Which isn't a home for keeping people alive that *nobody* wants. I guess they're right, there's just no sense to it.

—Don't take it so hard, Otto. We can relax for a couple of months and see how many of them pass on.

—When I think of how I said I was going to run the county as if it was my own business, I have to laugh. What kind of business is it that runs well if enough people die?

—Undertaker.

—It's no joke, Cecil. Fact is, if twenty people in the home give up the ghost in the next six months we're good managers and should be re-elected. If they live, we're no good. Maybe what we were really elected for is to see that they do die.

—Ah, now, Otto, it's not that bad. We're covered, and on the record. Let's forget the home till the next meeting; we have better things to talk about. By then we may come up with a new idea or two.

—I have my own idea right now.

4

(From the Cadie City *Messenger,* February 23)

. . . State Fire Marshal Robert McCluskey said that the fire evidently spread so rapidly that neither the additional fire escapes nor the firewall partitions mandated by his office in January would have saved the victims. The county commissioners had recently been granted a two-month extension on the installations, according to Commission Chairman Cecil Grimes, because of budgetary problems. Mr. Grimes, who had previously been taken briefly to Cadie County Hospital in a state of shock when he learned of the tragedy, declared that this information afforded him no relief from his feelings of grief induced by the holocaust. . . .

No residents of the home were believed to have survived the blaze, according to Commissioner Mary Zellerbach, except for the lone member of the staff on duty at the time, Howard Stingle. Mr. Stingle reported that he had no warning whatever of the fire until he saw the flames "going up all around me." Not only was it impossible to reach the fire-alarm bell, he said, but he barely had time to leap through the flames and the window of his ground-floor office, suffering multiple lacerations from the glass. . . .

Mr. McCloskey said that although he did not intend to prejudge the results of the investigation under way, it seemed fairly clear to him that although the sprinkler system had been recently inspected and approved it could not, even if functioning perfectly, have kept up with the suddenness and virulence of the flames. "I don't ever recall seeing a fire that moved so fast and hard," he said, "except maybe in one of the tent fires we used to see thirty–forty years ago." He refused to comment at this time on the possible origins of the blaze. "The only thing that comes to mind would be napalm or phosphorus used by an arsonist," he explained, "which would be unlikely. Arson is almost always for profit or insurance, and no one had anything to gain from this fire." He agreed with your reporter that there was always a "chance in a million" that it could have been set "by some nut," but indicated that in his professional judgment this could be ruled out as a practical possibility.

Chairman Grimes said that the Board of County Commissioners would meet to discuss the aftermath of the disaster as soon as Commissioner Otto Siebert, who was understood to have been out of town on a business trip at the time of the fire, returned. The only order of business at this time, he said, was the matter of burial arrangements for the victims. Many of their relatives had volunteered to underwrite private funeral costs, he said. "People will spend money for some

45

things, but not for others," said Mrs. Zellerbach, but declined to elaborate on her comment. . . .

• WELCOME to the club, Otto Siebert. You have acted courageously and decisively on your own logic. And in the months to come, you will justify your act to yourself in increasingly uncompromising terms, as you must.

Siebert is not the kind of man anyone would associate with extreme action in any area of his life, least of all in the so-called public sector. He is a lumber dealer, politically and economically conservative, a conscientious churchman (and a true believer), a man bearing all the stigmata of what a national politician a few years ago shrewdly labeled "middle America" and claimed for his own. There is nothing in his appearance, in his behavior, or in his *curriculum vitae* that catches the eye with a clue. But his burning of the county home is a reminder that today's easy-going version of American traditional fundamentalism conceals an implacable fanaticism that can erupt when its fault-line is disturbed.

Grimes and Mrs. Zellerbach certainly know what he did. By now they have diluted their first certain recognition of what must have happened into a vague and uneasy suspicion, which in turn will be diluted further and forgotten, except in an occasional bad dream. But, as Siebert sensed, what if they did talk? Who would believe them? And what could they prove?

Nobody would believe them. Siebert is safe for the same reason that prompted his sacrificial purge in the first place. Nobody *wants* to know.

CHAPTER SIX

1

Washington, Mar. 26—Gas industry representatives today denied the possibility of malfunction or negligence in the disastrous gas explosions that took the lives of upwards of 2,000 persons in Chicago's west side ghetto Thursday.

In a statement issued jointly today by a group of privately owned companies distributing gas for consumer use, the industry charged unnamed "extremist groups" with perpetrating "an act of terror aimed at fomenting civil disorder."

The statement, issued over the signatures of the agents for 72 gas companies maintaining offices here, flatly ruled out the chance of accident in the catastrophe as "technologically absurd." Speaking at a press conference called by the signatories, John R. Dalls of the Northeastern United Utilities Group urged investigation by the F.B.I. of leaders of the violent protest demonstrations that broke out in Chicago and six other cities following the blasts.

No comment was immediately forthcoming from William Francis Rooney, chairman of the *ad hoc* commission appointed by the President Saturday to investigate the explosions. Dr. Rooney, the President's principal adviser on environmental affairs, was scheduled to leave for Chicago to confer with community leaders in an effort to end the disturbances.

47

2

—I hope you know what you're doing, Frank.

—Oh, for God's sake! Of course I don't know what I'm doing, beyond a certain point. But I'm doing something, and I think it'll work. Christ, no wonder you liberals always manage to beat yourselves. You have to make so God-damned sure everything you do is right, and that it won't hurt anybody too much besides, you always run half a lap behind what would happen naturally anyway. Nothing personal, Henry, but we have to get out of the old liberal clichés if we want to see some change.

—That was gratuitous, Frank; you know I agree with you. Getting anything done is dangerous. All I want to know, if it's possible, is what the dangers are. I don't think our administration can afford to take another bad beating right now. The President will ask you the same question, and not so politely. He's already asked *me:* "Does Rooney really have a plan, or is he winging it again?"

—O.K., sorry. Anyway, here's what I'll propose, if I don't get a better idea before I get there. First, further condolences, more deep concern and grief from the President, the usual bag. But now we must look to the future, for the survivors, etc. Let us therefore seize this tragedy as an opportunity to guarantee that it won't happen again and show that America has the strength to rebuild, etc. O.K.? First, what do we do for the survivors? The figure we get is in the order of a hundred thousand. We have no place to put them. Mayor Finley has half of them bunked down in public buildings, theaters, halls, the works. The slob is efficient as hell when he has to be. The rest are squeezed in with friends, neighbors, nice people and so on. They can't keep up that way—but they'll have to. We'll have the Army throw up quonsets, temporaries, as fast as they can. Every doctor and nurse in the area has been conscripted for the duration. I'll propose we give every victim twenty-five dollars a week, including children, for an indefinite period, no questions asked. We'll use whatever lists that Finley can

48

come up with of who lives where and send out the money every day in armored trucks to distribution points all over the area. Then——

—Frank, it'll never work. Questions of identity, the chiseling——

—Chickenshit. *Of course* a lot of them won't see a penny of it. *Of course* there'll be more stealing and check-forging than you ever saw on welfare. But it doesn't matter. There's no perfect way to get things done in a sloppy world, Henry; we're lucky there's any way at all. The main thing is that most of them will be taken care of, to some extent, and that everybody knows the government is serious about doing something for them. That's part one. O.K.?

—I hope you're right, Frank.

—You know I'm right. For part two, we start the biggest building program anybody has ever seen. We clear out all the debris, and we start. And no cheap stuff. We build the west side of Chicago to last. With space, gardens, schools, factory sites, the whole bit. It's not that hard, just expensive. Figuring arbitrarily about ten thousand dollars per person unit, say a billion. Probably less. We issue a special tax-free bond to keep the cost down, and you know what? Eventually we get the money back. The rents will make it, even low ones. And that's not all.

—I'm listening.

—We use every damned one of the dispossessed people who wants to work. On the construction, doing something. And no bullshit from the building trades. This time they wouldn't dare. It takes a disaster to force reason down anybody's throat, you know that. The relief cost—three million a week, whatever it comes to, will taper off in a hurry once the building gets rolling.

—Very neat, Frank. Too neat, I think.

—Shit. And *that's* not all. Once the whole program becomes visible—the magnitude of it, not just the emergency patriotism—people will begin to ask questions. Serious questions.

—You can say that again.

—I don't think you're with it, Henry. I mean *this* kind of question, from you and your friends. Why should it take a disaster to solve the problems of decent housing for American slums? If we can spend this kind of money to rise to an emergency, why do we have to wait for the emergency? Why can't we do the same thing, rationally and less expensively, on purpose, without having to wait for all these poor bastards to get killed or homeless? Why can't we do the same thing for the whole country, say a hundred acres at a time in each city, efficiently and on a schedule? And on a schedule that the ghettos know is for real? And without their having to riot themselves to death to get any action out of The Man?

—Could be. I hope you're right. You sound so enthusiastic I could believe you set off those explosions yourself.

—Maybe I did.

—Very funny. But I have a serious question. Why in the world are you so sure that the Congress and everybody else involved will go along with a program of this size? They never have before, and we've had some bad situations before.

—Because this time they're scared to death, Henry. It's too big and too concentrated to talk away with oratory. This time enough of them *believe* their own riot-and-revolution stories, and they'll move. Some of the old conservatives will want to move faster than I do—just watch and see. You know I'm right, Henry. The President knows it too. That's the advantage of a *real* catastrophe—it gets action!

3

—Gentlemen, this is the program. I don't think I have to tell you that details will still have to be worked out, obviously. We were no more prepared for a disaster like this than you were. And when I tell you we welcome suggestions, you can believe me this time. Don't hold back. One thing I ask is that you keep your ideas on building, for example, separate from what you have in mind on, say, how the relief funds should be handled. Speed is of the essence. We'll have groups working on every aspect of the program, and we don't want them stepping over each other any more than you know they will anyway. And if you don't like the program at all, or have a better one, speak up. We're not locked into this yet, but we will be pretty soon.

—Dr. Rooney, you have talked about this most ambitious program as if it were all set and all that was left was doing it. What about the President and the Congress? How can we count on the Congress?

—The President considers what happened here a major national emergency and has authorized me to say he will do whatever is necessary to meet it. As an old hand in politics, I cannot imagine any serious opposition under the circumstances. Leaders of both parties have told me they will go along with whatever it takes. They will even cut back military appropriations if necessary—so you *know* they're serious.

—What about the investigation into the causes of the explosions, Frank?

—First things first, Mr. Mayor. We have a force of experts getting organized to get the answers there, and we have a group from the Department of Justice looking into the charges of sabotage and so on. But the most urgent matter is taking care of the people who need taking care of. We're luckier than doctors. We don't have to wait for a diagnosis to start the process of cure.

—The gas companies say it *has* to be sabotage. Isn't it important to find out right away? What if whoever did it repeats in New York or Cleveland?

—Off the record, gentlemen? O.K.? I don't want to jump to conclusions, of course, but based on what we know already I'd say the chances of sabotage are minuscule. Don't misunderstand—I'm not charging the gas companies with negligence or deliberate self-serving misrepresentation. At least I have no basis for it at this time. But there is an obvious question of the adequacy of their

51

fail-safe system, so far as protecting us from the spreading of local accidents is concerned. We'll find out in due course.

—As another old hand in politics, Frank, I think you're in for a real blast of pressure from other cities for similar programs. They'll say: Do we have to have a disaster to get the help we need for rebuilding?

—They may indeed, Mr. Mayor. We'll take it as it comes. Fortunately for all you gentlemen here, that's our problem, not yours. Sufficient unto the day. Now, then, let's get down to setting up a little organization table. Nothing elaborate, just enough so that everyone here knows who's responsible for what. I imagine Mayor Finley has some ideas on it, so let's hear from him first. . . .

4

—I tell you, Frank, I'm still high. Like I'm ready for another job just like this.

—Then it's a good thing I don't have one for you. Too much comes too fast in a deal like this. Why don't you take a vacation? A cruise in the Caribbean, or an African safari. Something where you can keep out of crowded cities.

—A psychologist too, aren't you, Frank? No, it won't work. I'll come down, in time. But what about you, Mister Cool?

—Hell, my part of the action is just beginning. How I handle this program will make me or break me. I want my place in history, Chuck, and I intend to get it.

—And you don't care how. You scare the shit out of me, Frank.

—Come on, Chuck. Are you coming down with a malignant case of sober second thoughts?

—Maybe. No, I guess not. Assuming it works out the way we figured.

—It will. . . . You think I'm a pretty Machiavellian character.

—You are. Which is not all bad, in my book. No, all that worries me about you—so I don't think about it—is what you may dream up next year and the year after that, whether you may get hooked into the bag of what's good for Rooney is good for everybody, so anything goes.

—Shit. At the risk of sounding vain, but I don't give a damn, I know more history, where it counts, than anybody you ever heard of, boy. I want my name to stand as the guy who rebuilt the cities, who ended poverty, who made it possible for others to finish the job. I want to be Rooney the life-giver, not Rooney the terrible. And that's the way it's going to be.

—Still——

—"Still!" You mean you never know what a megalomaniac will do next time. Relax, Chuck. My great saving grace is a sense of perspective. And a sense of what people will take and what they won't.

—They won't take killing two thousand for political purposes.

—Won't they, though? Yes, they will. Eventually. When they're satisfied that the purposes are acceptable. And, just as important, when there's enough distance between them and the killing. In space or in time—it doesn't matter. Do you know about Skopje?

—Who?

—A city in Yugoslavia. It was destroyed by an earthquake in 1963. One thousand seventy killed officially, probably more. One hundred thirty-five thousand homeless, more or less. By 1970, only seven years later, it was a new, beautiful, prosperous city, a showplace. You know what one of the happy townsfolk said? He'd lost his family. "Each town in Macedonia could use an earthquake every twenty years or so." Doesn't that tell you something?

—Maybe, if you're not inventing it. You told me before you got the idea from Vietnam.

—So I did. We accepted—how many?—sixty thousand dead Americans, millions of dead Vietnamese. Everybody accepted it, Chuck, everybody, even those who said we should all be hanged as war criminals. They accepted it because they had to accept it, because it was there. They'll accept this operation, too, Chuck, if they ever have to be told, because the purpose will have been accomplished. In Vietnam there hadn't even been any purpose. Patriotism, stop Communism, the usual shit—translation: it's official, it's acceptable, it's O.K. That's all there was, there wasn't any more. Here at least the purpose will be tangible, something they can see and use and appreciate. An extra bonus.

—That's too rational, Frank. Since when has the body politic become rational?

—It hasn't. But it still needs an excuse. But that's all it needs.

—I guess so. You know what I'd like to do next? Work on the building program. Not so exciting, but I'm like everybody else. I like to see something tangible, too.

—Good. Take a break, look it over, name your spot.

—I have to hand it to you, Frank. You're not afraid of your own logic. You want something done, you go the shortest way.

—Naturally. But I don't recommend it for everybody. I trust *myself.*

• DR. FRANK ROONEY is a very cute operator, whatever one thinks of his urban renewal plan. But it's hard not to feel that he will overextend himself at some point, or even that he may have already done so. Every precedent suggests that his self-touted "sense of perspective" cannot survive the successful consummation of his megalomania. History, common sense, psychological casebooks, and general experience all conspire to refute him.

Still, despite the magnitude of what he has committed, one cannot charge him with losing touch with "reality." For the reality of the great social processes involved in the administration of political or economic power has little in common with the sense of proportion that defines sanity in the behavior of individuals. When a private person attempts to apply an institutional rationale to his own immediate affairs he is asking for trouble. But what he may do as the authorized agent of an institution is subject only to political constraints.

Up to this point you have read six small stories about killings, told in barebones dialogue and newspaper excerpts. In each episode, the impetus for the proposed killing has been a presumed and substantial net social benefit. Self-aggrandizement, where present, has been rationalized or disguised. The killings have not been inspired by private passion or profit. Their perpetrators have acted as self-appointed spokesmen for certain institutions. They have in common the conviction that the social problems that concern them now require Draconian solutions, and the boldness to assert the institutional authority and the sense of moral immunity their actions imply.

But even when their interests are not entirely parochial, their resources are relatively limited, at this point even Rooney's. In the chapters that follow, those who have greater power to instigate social change will exercise it.

PART TWO

CHAPTER SEVEN

1

Detroit, Mar. 30—Automobile industry representatives announced today that "completely pollution-free" vehicles will go into production in the Fall of next year.

John P. Haynes, president of North American Motors, said that the changeover from conventional automobiles would be complete, so far as all four major U.S. producers were concerned. Production of current models will continue for the next year and a quarter, he said, at which time all companies will devote themselves exclusively to final retooling for the new models, which is expected to take only about three additional months.

The announcement caught trade observers here by surprise, since the industry had consistently maintained until now that an economically practical pollution-free automobile was at least ten years away. They agreed, however, that the remarkably effective secrecy surrounding the unexpected progress of research and testing for the new vehicle could be readily justified pending recent Congressional assurance of the subsidies provided in the Clean Air Incentives Act.

Mr. Haynes refused to divulge at this time how the new cars would be propelled, saying only that details of their design would be publicized "in due course." He implied, however, that the effect of the changeover on the oil industry would be much less than might be expected, prompting speculation that some type of oil-powered "packaged energy" might be used.

His reassurance was confirmed by oil industry spokesmen, who indicated that they had been in consultation with the auto manufacturers on the new development. Their statement, issued simultaneously after the close of all major U.S. stock exchanges, was expected to mitigate possible panic selling of oil stocks tomorrow.

Mr. Haynes also revealed that a cross-licensing agreement on every aspect of the new auto technology had been approved by the antitrust division of the Department of Justice that would enable all automobile producers to compete on even terms in the distribution of the pollution-free vehicles.

Most independent technical experts consulted here believe that the new cars will be powered by an adaptation of the electricity-producing fuel cells used in the space program. A few, however, lean toward steam, in view of Mr. Haynes's assurances to the oil industry, although they acknowledge that an oil-burning steam engine could not be accurately described as "completely" pollution-free. One consultant suggested that compressed and liquefied gas, possibly nitrogen, handled in easily replaceable pellet tanks, might be used. None of the experts reached believe nuclear power will be directly involved.

In response to a question, Mr. Haynes said that all producers would continue to manufacture replacement parts, including conventional gasoline engines, for existing automobiles for "as long as necessary, and certainly for at least five years." He indicated that engine production would probably be concentrated in the companies' Canadian plants.

2

GORDON CROCKER: A wild guessing game was set off in the nation's capital yesterday following the auto industry's announcement of the advent of the "clean" automobile. Unlike Detroit, where most speculation centered on the technology of the new cars, Washington has been more intrigued by the economic and political implications of the breakthrough, and the role, if any, played by government agencies in its development. Observers here wonder how such a far-flung project—almost certainly involving hundreds or even thousands of persons—could have advanced as it did without any known leak to the press or public.

Although no definable schools of thought have yet formed on these questions, considerable skepticism was evidenced among those long active in the anti-automobile-pollution movement. We take you now to our Washington studios, where Wilfrid Hartley is talking with Peter Masterman, director of the Joint Steering Committee for Clean Air Organizations, the principal "public interest" lobbyist for the clean air cause.

MR. HARTLEY: According to yesterday's story from Detroit, Mr. Masterman, it would appear that your crusade may be coming to a successful conclusion.

MR. MASTERMAN: I'm not so sure, Mr. Hartley. I don't want to prejudge the industry's latest sortie into public relations, but until the hard facts of what they are really going to do are put on the table, we are not about to start dancing in the streets. We have always said that the industry could put out a pollution-free car whenever it wanted to or was forced to, without waiting for any so-called technological breakthrough, but I don't yet know that they have.

MR. HARTLEY: What is the reason for your skepticism?

MR. MASTERMAN: Well, the deal they seem to have made with the oil industry is disturbing. It may well mean, for instance, that the pollution now on the streets will be transferred to some kind of local power stations, perhaps existing gas stations. If this is true, it would still be a step forward, but it would not solve the basic problem.

61

MR. HARTLEY: Do you have any information about the new engines, or the fuel they will use, that leads you to say that?

MR. MASTERMAN: Only what I can guess or infer from Mr. Haynes's statement. There's also the smell of a treasury raid in the air—considering the timing. We will insist that the Clean Air Administration conduct a thorough and public examination of the industry's figures on the changeover before they issue a blank check to Detroit. They've sold us phony bills of goods before. Remember those pollution-reducing devices a few years back? They barely cut down the poison enough to offset the increase in cars and trucks on the road.

MR. HARTLEY: Thank you, Mr. Masterman. And now, back to New York and Gordon Crocker.

MR. CROCKER: George Hellman, director of the Clean Air Administration, told us today that he would make no comment on the industry announcement until after the C.A.A. had a chance to confer with auto industry officials. We learned elsewhere, however, that the news was as much of a surprise to the C.A.A. as to the general public.

A spokesman for the antitrust division of the Department of Justice said that the cross-licensing agreement referred to by Mr. Haynes had been approved in general terms over a year ago, but that it included no specific technical plans for the propulsion system of the new cars.

3

—So you think we left you out on a limb. We don't agree, Hellman. If you had known exactly what we were going to do, the pressure would have been more than you could have lived with. You can't tell me for a minute that your office wouldn't have leaked. Now, I'm not saying that ignorance is bliss, but it sure as hell eases responsibility. You should thank us for leaving you out of the preliminaries.

—I don't agree with you, Mr. Haynes, but it's water under the bridge now. Why you should expect us to appreciate being made to look like fools I don't know. If you think it will win points for you in Congress you're wrong. If you think any congressmen except those you own already will buy the idea that the public will be protected by your good will without regulation by us you're more naive than you think *we* are. If credit is due you'll get it. We won't fight you for it. But if it's another snow job you'll lose both ways.

—Christ, you guys are sensitive. Did it ever occur to you that what we tell you might be exactly what we mean?

—Yes, it has. Has occured to us, that is. But it's never happened yet. All right, what's the story? Or are you going to be mysterious with us too?

—A little bit. We can't tell you everything until our lawyers give us the go-ahead on process and patent rights. But we can tell you enough for you to relax.

—Not likely, Mr. Haynes. But let's have it.

—Not so fast. Even the general picture has to be off the record at this time. If anything specific about the propulsion system comes out in the press, one question will lead to another and it will be damned difficult to hold back what we have to hold back for a little longer.

—Look, Mr. Haynes, if important legal questions still aren't settled, how can you be sure you're ready to make the big move?

—Because we *are* sure, damn it. This is very funny. I can see it in the papers now. "C.A.A. chief urges delay in production of pollution-free car."

—All right, all right. You know we don't want delay. We want only credible assurance that your announcement is on the level both ways. That the car is really pollution-free, and that you are ready to make the change next year.

—You have it. Now, off the record. The system will use an "energy package." It will consist of two parts. One will be liquid oxygen. The other will be a new kind of petroleum-based fuel, which the oil industry can and will make. We developed it, incidentally; they didn't. It will burn completely. The by-product, or exhaust, as we used to think of it, will be almost pure carbon dioxide. Most of it will be recovered chemically, in solid form, so that what goes into the air won't be more than you'd get from a team of horses. You can run one of these engines in a closed garage for a long time before it even feels stuffy.

—Then it will be an internal combustion engine?

—Yes and no. The fuel will burn, not explode. It will be quiet, too.

—I see you're not ready to give out. What about this solid waste? Carbonates, I suppose. What do you do with them?

—Not carbonates, but you're close. Hell, you dispose of them like you do any other garbage. But they're clean, and easy to handle, like clinkers. Hell, what do you want? We're taking the crud out of the air. It has to go somewhere.

—Can it be used for something? In building, for instance?

—Oh, probably. The oil people are working on it. But one thing at a time, Hellman. Even if the garbage turns out to be nothing but garbage, we're still way ahead. And we can always remove the CO_2 collector and let it go into the air, in a pinch. But you wouldn't want that—even though we'd still be miles ahead of where we're at now.

—No, I wouldn't.

—We thought not. But you should know that the CO_2 collector will add to the cost. And you might as well also know there's another negative. There will be more pollution from the oil refineries, at least until they lick that problem. The air will be worse in their areas. But the ratio will be about one to twenty, so there will be a net gain overall of about 95 per cent. I'm telling you this now, so you can be prepared for some tough politics from the people who live downwind of the refineries. But that's your department.

—I see. What else comes with the package?

—High cost, of course. You'll get some flak on this, but it

64

shouldn't be too tough. People will expect to pay for clean air. If they don't, the whole business is a joke.

—All right. How much?

—Fuel cost of the new cars will run about triple to begin with. It will come down in time; depends on how well you can bargain with the oil people. Maintenance is bound to be higher at first, but that should come down to less than we have now, after we work the bugs out.

—What about the cost of the cars themselves?

—About double at first. We're not greedy. We want to amortize the changeover in five years. Then we'll get competitive, one way or another. In the long run, it won't be too high. Under the Act, we expect you to subsidize 75 per cent of the difference. If you run into trouble on cost you can talk persuasively about the savings on public health, and so on, which will be far greater.

—Do you have figures?

—Hell, no, it's just a slogan. It might be true, but what's the difference? It's right on principle.

—I'm happy to see you've become an evangelist for clean air, Mr. Haynes. I seem to recall your making a big pitch to the effect that automobile-exhaust pollution was merely a harmless nuisance, and not so long ago, either.

—We all learn, Hellman, each in his own way. With us, capital investment is the big educator. The university of hard cash.

Off the record, for us this time, Mr. Haynes, you are a cynical son of a bitch.

—Glad to be of service. Now, there's just one more small problem. If you don't mind our recessing for about an hour—for lunch, maybe?—I'd like to hold off discussion of it until our man who's better informed on it than I am gets here. O.K.? Incidentally, you won't need your technical group for this—excuse me, gentlemen—I will have only this one adviser along and I think you'll be perfectly safe from rape if you don't outnumber us. O.K.? Please.

—I want you to meet Fred Hermanson, who has been our special consultant for the problem we want to discuss with you. Fred, this, as you know, is George Hellman, our Clean Air Administrator, and his deputy, William Riley.

—I've met Mr. Riley, Mr. Haynes.

—Good. Let's begin. Now, I told you the problem I want to bring to your attention is not technical, and I implied it did not lend itself constructively to a large committee meeting like the one we had this morning. Let me qualify this. The source of the problem is technical, but the problem itself, as we see it, is not. You might call it political, or even philosophical.

—We're listening, Mr. Haynes.

—Superficially, you might say it's a question of safety. But we feel it goes beyond the usual piddling design problems, crash-resistance and so on, which we can normally leave to junior engineers. The fact is, gentlemen, that the new cars will be unusually dangerous.

—Now, what the hell! You told us only two hours ago that you finally had the real thing. Now it turns out you've been leading us down the garden path again. If the car is unusually dangerous, how can you say you're ready to go into production?

—Hold it, Hellman. I mean only that it's dangerous in an unusual way. It won't contribute to more highway accidents; if anything, it will reduce them, since there will probably be fewer drivers. No, this has to do with the energy package. It holds enormous pressures. It has to be started up correctly, and the unusual danger is that if it is not started correctly it can blow up and kill the driver.

—This is ridiculous.

—Not so fast. It isn't really *more* dangerous than ordinary driving; the kind of mistake the driver can make in starting up is no more inherent in the design of the car than the mistake he can make when he turns the steering wheel the wrong way at seventy miles an hour and runs into a tree.

—But it's an added danger, since the same percentage of drivers will run into trees as before. If your new danger is equal, quantitatively, car accidents—or is it deaths?—will double.

—Deaths. I have no reason to believe there will be the same number of accidents of this kind than what we have already, or more, or fewer. But I do know that the accident rate from energy-package mishandling will decline rapidly. The kind of people who will be victims will weed themselves out quickly. And before you get too upset, let me tell you that in the long run this particular hazard will *reduce* the number of highway deaths.

—Oh, for God's sake. I suppose you mean that most people will just be afraid to drive at all. What are you trying to sell us, Mr. Haynes?

—Please. Listen carefully. The only people who will get killed from improper starting are people who shouldn't be driving anyway, the ones who *cause* most road accidents. As I said, there is nothing inherently dangerous in the starting device itself—provided the driver follows the extremely simple rules for using it. Those who are not morons, or irresponsible, or drunk, will be in no danger—ever. Neither will passengers. On the road, a responsible driver can be killed by someone else's mistake. But not here. Ever.

—How can you be so sure of that?

—Ah, that's better. I'm glad to see you're beginning to ask reasonable questions. The chief reason is that we have deliberately located the package where only the driver can be affected by a mishandling. There is no place we could have put it that would have been safe for everyone, obviously, or we would have done so. Our only other option would have been to endanger a passenger, because of a driver's stupid mistake, which we rejected. I'm going to ask Fred here to take over my end of this discussion, on our longer-range reasoning about the problem.

67

—Just a minute, Mr. Haynes. I will assume that for some reason you were unable to devise a satisfactory safety device, or you would have done so. But couldn't you have programed what you called the "very simple" starting procedure into an automatic system?

—Certainly. By combining two ignition steps into one switch. And less complicated than an automatic transmission, too. But no automatic system is ever remotely foolproof, as we know better than anyone, and although it's quite possible that an automatic system *might* lead to fewer accidents of this sort—but only at first, if so—we rejected it. First of all, quite frankly, the responsibility for malfunction of the automatic system might be ours, legally, and we don't want it. Second, the victim would be just as likely to be a responsible driver as not. . . . Fred?

—I wanted to say something else about safety devices. We *have* built-in safety devices, Mr. Hellman, but we were afraid to cover every step of the ignition in this way. If we did, drivers would inevitably come to depend on them entirely, instead of exercising their own very simple responsibilities. There would be an occasional malfunction, and—poof. The penalty is too severe. It's not like an automatic choke or transmission. If they don't work, you have trouble, and in rare circumstances you can be endangered, but only from secondary causes. Remember, Mr. Hellman, we are not talking about spaceships, or even airplanes, where professional mechanics check out all systems regularly. We are talking about common automobiles and millions of common persons driving them, who cannot be expected to maintain their components with any degree of dependability. For a responsible driver—not a mechanic—no safety device can possibly be as reliable as his own knowledge that he must not turn switch B for at least two seconds after he has turned switch A. Our instructions will say five seconds, of course, though at some loss of efficiency. We had considered using a simple time lock, which we would have mentioned only in our mechanics' manuals because we wouldn't have wanted anyone to depend on it for their lives. But we finally rejected it, for the reason I mentioned. The only people who will get killed are those who are unusually irresponsible. Statistically, it should not be too big a deal, although I can't give you any firm estimates. It is only the *nature* of the risk that makes it unusual, and perhaps important.

—I don't like it, Mr. Hermanson. I don't like it at all. What do you think, Bill?

—I think we should hear the rest of what Mr. Hermanson has to say, George. It could be that he is being deliberately over-conservative about the dangers.

—Precisely. I think I am, at any rate. Nevertheless, even if the deaths from malstarting are statistically no more significant than from, say, exploding gas tanks, there is bound to be an uproar unless you cooperate with us in publicizing, explaining, and justifying the hazard.

—Justifying!

—Yes, Mr. Hellman. In my work I happen to have had considerable experience with problems involving mortal risk. I am convinced that people will accept almost any risk imaginable if they are provided a rationale for it and know they are expected to accept it. In this case, for instance, I think it would be a great mistake to be defensive. I think that if people know that this particular danger is a good thing for them they will be happy to accept it.

—How in hell are you going to persuade anybody that he should like the idea that he may be blown up because it's *good* for him? This is too much.

—Let me explain, Mr. Hellman. Mr. Riley can assure you that I am not given to make rash statements.

—That's true, George. You won't get PR stuff from Fred.

—I try to take the long view of any problem I deal with, Mr. Hellman, if I can. I would like you to accept the premise, to begin with, that we are all interested in the optimum benefit that might be derived from any change. Agreed? And this new car will be a major change, make no mistake about it. Now, we may differ on definition of benefit, but for the sake of argument let's say we would like the introduction of our new car to provide the greatest good for the greatest number, more or less.

—Well, obviously. That's the point of cleaning up car pollution in the first place. What has that to do with drivers getting killed?

—Exactly. The principal point of the change the new car will make is that millions of people will live better and longer than they would have without it. This alone would justify quite a few lives lost, as a small price for it, don't you think? But let's ignore that aspect of our problem and consider the cleaner air as a free net benefit. The fact is that even without *that* benefit the killing off of irresponsible drivers is in itself a very good thing for the general public. I think I can prove to you—*a priori*—that the kinds of drivers who will make the ridiculously simple mistake in our starting procedure that will kill them are the kinds who are most likely, even certain, to kill or injure others on the road, or in other activities. So consider the danger to the individual driver who may be killed by such a mistake as a safety device to reduce the random casualties of society as a whole.

—Mr. Hermanson, by your kind of upside-down reasoning I could argue that the sixty thousand people killed on the highways every year, the hundred and fifty thousand crippled, the four and a half million injured, are also good things.

—Almost, but not quite. Not quite, because such a high proportion of the highway victims—unlike those who will be killed by improper starting of the new car—are innocent. Since you make this point, let me remind you that society is knowingly willing to kill these people every year as a price for the benefits accruing from fast transportation. If it were forbidden to manufacture cars that could go more than twenty miles an hour it would save—who knows?—forty or fifty thousand lives a year. And everybody knows this, really. But no one is willing to save them. The same thing is true, of course, with different figures and in different ways, for almost every aspect of what most of us would agree is progress—

technological or scientific advances from which society receives a net benefit. As the old saying goes, there is no such thing as a free lunch.

—Mr. Hermanson, I understand your point. But there is a moral difference between accepting a certain level of risk that applies to all of us more or less equally and singling out certain kinds of people to take all the risk. I know we do it anyway, especially in war, but that doesn't make it right. And why do you refer to those who are killed on the highways through no fault of their own as "innocent?" Sure they're innocent, but you imply that the poor slobs who'll get killed because they make a simple mistake in starting your car are guilty. Guilty of what?

—Guilty of being the kind of people who endanger the lives and safety of other, Mr. Hellman. This guilt is pragmatic, not moral. I prefer the word "irresponsible," but guilty will do. If your child is killed by an incompetent driver, Mr. Hellman, would it make you feel better that the driver is a good-natured fool rather than a deliberate murderer? I doubt it. A car is a weapon, Mr. Hellman, even though it wasn't invented to be one. So is almost everything men manufacture. We kill people with our products, though not deliberately. It would be better, I agree, if we could devise a way to prevent the kind of people I'm talking about from driving cars, using tools, lighting fires, turning on electric current, or doing anything else that can be hazardous to others. But we can't, because no one can function in today's world without these weapons, unless he's a vegetable. As for the moral difference you spoke of: I do not accept letting chance govern who survives and who does not, when one is in a position to make a choice in behalf of net social gain, as a moral decision. You don't want to share responsibility for the deaths of those I call guilty. But in doing nothing about them you share responsibility for the deaths of the innocent. The only difference is that in doing nothing you feel protected by the anonymity of not taking an affirmative step. Once you understand these implications you are making a choice, willy-nilly,

71

whether you want to or not. You can't be neutral.

—Mr. Hermanson, this is casuistry, and I don't accept it for a minute. I'm not sharing responsibility for the deaths of anyone. What you are arguing, in plainer language, is that since a lot of people get killed by automobiles I am delinquent if I don't exercise my opportunity to pass judgment on what class of drivers are to be destroyed. I have no right to do anything of the kind, and neither do you. On what basis do you presume that those you call irresponsible have less right to survive than others? On what authority?

—I don't think I'm getting through to you, Mr. Hellman. Let me put it another way. I acknowledge responsibility for what I don't do as well as for what I do. My criterion in this case is quantitative. Eliminating the small group of truly dangerous drivers will save more lives than it will lose. I have no subjective bias against them. Only against their function. We live surrounded by man-made weapons—cars, drugs, appliances, foods, what have you. I will feel safer, and so will you, if those whose incompetence to use one of the most dangerous of these weapons kill themselves instead of threatening me. I think this is a reasonable and objective bias.

—Mr. Hermanson, we're getting nowhere. You make broad assumptions.

—Let me go further. I would suggest that the operational dangers implicit in technology—as in driving a car—are not bad things. I'm speaking for myself now, not for Mr. Haynes.

—That's O.K. Fred. This is all off the record anyway. I'll talk. Hellman knows that the element of risk has always been one of the subconscious appeals we've made to the automobile buyer. We have to deny it publicly, of course, but this is the big reason we fought safety devices in general. Not cost. They didn't cost that much. Fred was going to say, Hellman, that people need and want a sense of danger, a sense of pitting their skill and courage against the environment, which is lacking in their lives. Something that makes them depend on their own actions and decisions for survival. Like the wheel of a car. Something that reminds them in their daily lives that there are lions and tigers out there. Everybody needs this, Hellman, not just the pistols who go in for dangerous sports. We furnish it, always have. And we're proud of it, damn it. We keep some excitement in everybody's workaday routine. Not too much, of course, because that would be self-defeating. But enough.

—Your candor, after all these years, is very interesting, Mr. Haynes. So tell me this. If you think making a car risky to drive is essentially a good thing—up to a point, as you say—why are you cooperating in cutting down on exhaust poisoning? If it's that beneficial, why not leave it alone? Why not just keep snowing us about the technical difficulties? Why the change of heart? Certainly not because of the subsidies you're going to get from the Clean Air Incentives Act.

—Your sarcasm is unworthy of you, Hellman. Of course we were waiting for the subsidies, and we never concealed it. But your smart-ass remarks miss the point again. You're confusing the danger from exhaust pollution—which is passive, a question of exposure—with the active danger of driving, where you, personally, in the driver's seat, have to cope with the irresponsible son of a bitch who may be barreling out at you from the next intersection. You're making the same mistake the research man from Ethyl made back in 1970, when we decided it was time to put them out of business. He screamed about how we killed more people than they did—and in front of reporters, if you please. His boss apologized for him later, but he was right. Yet he was really wrong where it counted. You get home safely after fighting your way through drunken drivers, loose animals, blowouts going around a curve in heavy traffic—you get some satisfaction, you've made it again, you've licked the bastards. But there was no satisfaction in getting lead poisoning! Once enough people got to know about it, and got worried, we had to get rid of it. Same thing now, of course.

73

—Mr. Haynes, if you don't mind some more of my unworthy sarcasm, what kind of line are you giving me now? A few minutes ago your Mr. Hermanson was telling us how deeply concerned you were to make driving safer for the average driver. By making it deadly dangerous for the "irresponsible" types who couldn't follow simple instructions. All for the general public safety, of course. Now you say danger is good, risk is great for morale, people need to take chances in driving. If so, then why all this guff about safety over the long run? Make up your mind and spare me from more lectures on my moral responsibility to kill off stupid drivers.

—All right. Tell him, Fred.

—Very well. Mr. Hellman, everything I told you is true. I am convinced that our starting procedure *will* reduce highway accidents over the long run. This is not inconsistent with our belief that the current level of danger in highway driving is a good thing. We are not trying to persuade you to agree with us that it is. We are simply being honest with you. More candid than we need to be, and you should respect this, I think. The argument I gave you to justify the hazard of the new car was to make it easier for you to cope with the difficulties you may have when this hazard is revealed. Our firm advice to you is to be affirmative about it, and I have shown you how you can.

—In other words, you've been giving me a cover story. No, thanks. You can do your own covering for yourself. I want no part of it.

—Damn it, Hellman, you don't seem to get the point. If you fight us on this—which you can do—you'll lose. People will accept the danger, and they won't accept your blocking a pollution-free car when they know it's been offered and available. Can't you get that through your bureaucratic skull? You think our line is self-serving. Of course it is. But it will also serve you and it will serve the public health.

—Bill, what do you make of all this garbage?

—George, I'm sorry, but I agree with them. In principle, that is; I'd want to have more real data on just how dangerous this starting procedure is. But assuming it's as they say, I think we should go along. We have a mandate to get a clean car on the road. If the Congress or anyone else thinks the price is too steep, let *them* overrule us.

—You had something to add, Fred?

—Yes. Speaking for myself, I go much further than Mr. Haynes on the desirability of keeping driving dangerous. He's satisfied with the *status quo*. I'm not. I'm in favor of much more weeding out of population, on whatever rational, objective basis offers itself. This is one of them. I think it's necessary socially. I'm not so interested in the psychological motivations Mr. Haynes spoke of. The world, even the United States, is becoming overcrowded. Functionally, not physically. The natural mechanisms are not working. I mean the traditional ways in which population is controlled—famine, disease, war, and so forth. If we don't take as many aspects of population control into our own hands as we can, the end will be explosive. I don't want to wait for it. I want reason to prevail. I——

—Mr. Hermanson, excuse the interruption, but I am familiar with your point of view. I respect it, but I don't agree with it. If you will be kind enough to leave the details of your starting procedure hazards with us, along with the rest, we will discuss them in confidence with our experts, and we will get back to you as soon as we can to tell you what line we will take. I don't think any purpose will be served by more of this kind of discussion. Give us the data, and we'll take it from there.

5

Washington, Apr. 8—The Clean Air Administration is reserving judgment on the new "pollution-free" vehicles announced by Detroit last week.

William J. Riley, deputy director of the agency, said today

that although the information he obtained at a meeting April 3 with an industry group headed by North American Motors President John P. Haynes was "encouraging," the C.A.A. would not be prepared to evaluate the new automobiles until complete technical data were received and examined.

C.A.A. Director George Hellman added that it appeared that the new cars would call for substantial changes in national driving habits and patterns. It was even possible, he intimated, that new licensing requirements for drivers might be instituted as a condition of certification of the new automobiles. He declined, however, to amplify his remarks at this time.

Mr. Haynes, reached by telephone in Detroit, declined in turn to comment on Mr. Hellman's statement. He said that he hoped to be able to release "reasonably complete" information about the new cars to the general public within the next two or three weeks. However, another industry official closely associated with Mr. Haynes, who asked to remain anonymous, expressed astonishment at Mr. Hellman's suggestion that drivers might have to be relicensed. He attributed the C.A.A. chief's remark to a "misunderstanding" of the industry's preliminary description of the new car's propulsion system at last week's conference.

Peter Masterman, coordinator of the "clean air lobby" here, said that Mr. Hellman's reservations confirmed his first impression that the new car might be a "public relations stunt." He called on Mr. Hellman to "make a full disclosure of everything he knows about the so-called pollution-free car without further delay," and charged that the industry's "unwarranted secrecy" about its propulsion system should be investigated by the Congress.

• HAYNES and Hermanson are lying. The starting procedure will kill many more people than they imply; they exploit the fact that in this context understatement is expected of them. Haynes is accustomed to rationalizing whatever line of reasoning he thinks will work to his advantage: one does not become the chief operating officer of a giant corporation without demonstrating, among other things, a superior capacity for expressing plausible falsehoods in behalf of corporate and personal interests. He does this effectively, because he has no difficulty in "believing" what he thinks will be advantageous for him to believe.

He and the other automobile makers could perfectly well have arranged to install the simple time lock Hermanson mentioned, and it could have been close enough to foolproof to reduce the starting fatalities to a minimum. But their routine concern for their legal responsibility in cases of malfunction—an indeterminate cost factor—made it possible for Hermanson to sell them a much bigger bill of goods.

Hermanson has moved forward in his operations. No longer merely accepting or rejecting commissions for killing that meet the moral standards of his group, he is now initiating and developing major programs of mass killing. He has become, in fact, an evangelist for death as a social purifier. He and his associates have constructed an elaborate social philosophy in support of selective genocide that only begins with the simplistic argument he put to Hellman.

Their longer-term objective is more ambitious than to kill off x thousands of the "socially negative" drivers, as they describe the expendables among themselves. They want to create, bit by bit, a climate of public opinion that will receive the kind of discussion held with Hellman as a familiar, no longer shocking, posing of alternatives.

The strategy has a lot going for it. Since the car is in fact clean, the C.A.A. will, on reflection, desist from going beyond its specific authority (air pollution) by trying to interfere with its development. With the dangerous starting procedure included as an inseparable part of the package the C.A.A. will be placed in a position of having to justify it, very much along the lines suggested by Hermanson. The propriety of endangering the "irresponsible" in behalf of the greater good will then go on the agenda of public debate, at least in some form.

And then what? Hermanson's group has other plans to legitimize the issue. But they may be superfluous. The temper of the times is on their side, a point that comes up again and again. Public discussion of "overpopulation," of the possibilities inherent in nuclear weapons, of the fact that the limits to human life on the planet have been brought within sight by man's abuse of his physical environment, etc., etc., etc., is already well developed. Doctrines once associated only with neo-Malthusian cranks and war-gamers lusting for Doomsday have been taken over by scientists and moralists of impeccable credentials. Already the question, it appears, is no longer *whether* the species is in danger, but *how* it can survive. Therefore, why not consider . . .?

To get back to the clean car: Hellman of course senses what is going on, except for Hermanson's part of the game, but is trapped nonetheless. How Hermanson got to the automobile manufacturers as he did, and how the group even managed to spot Riley in the C.A.A. hierarchy is exemplar of how far cool and competent operators can go by truly understanding and effectively exploiting institutional self-interest. But that story is not sufficiently germane to *this* book.

CHAPTER EIGHT

1

—Ladies and gentlemen, I imagine you are wondering why, for the first time in the history of McCallum and Parker, we are holding a press conference to introduce a new product. As you know, we have always been, and we still are, what is called an "ethical" drug house. This word, as I hope you also know, is not intended to cast aspersions on the manufacturers of drugs sold over the counter to the general public. It means, essentially, that we make prescription drugs and that we advertise only to physicians. In making this announcement, therefore, we are departing from our normal practice—of over ninety years' standing—for what we consider good cause. I think you will agree that it is.

—Mr. Henry! There have been rumors that you are announcing a cure for cancer. Is that it?

—No, it is not. If you don't mind, I will proceed by telling you what the product is and what it does, and I will then be glad to answer questions. . . . The new product is one that some people might consider, on the whole, useful as a cure for cancer. But I don't wish to seem to exaggerate, so I will say it is not. . . . It might be described, although not adequately, as a qualitatively different kind of tranquilizer. Its effect, however, goes far beyond that of any such drugs now available, which are basically sedatives. It relieves anxiety and tension, as they do, but it has other properties that make it truly unique. It is not soporific. It is not in any way a depressant. It does not affect acuity of judgment, as other tranquilizers and stimulants all do. It has an affirmative action. By this I mean, in layman's language, it makes you feel good, not merely relaxed; it creates a noticeable, but wholly rational, euphoria. It is an antidepressant as well as an ataractic, and although it stimulates both mental and physical activity, it does so without any of the nervous excitation associated with stimulants. Finally, it has one additional property that it shares, so far as I know, with no other conventional drug. I would call it an anti-aggressive. It eliminates feelings of hostility, as well as all impulses to commit aggressive acts. I certainly do not have to spell out the implications of this property to you, ladies and gentlemen. One more thing. There do not appear to be any contra-indications to its use. Anyone can take it, regardless of cardiovascular condition, metabolic abnormality, or any other aspect of his medical history. For this reason we will ask the Federal Drug Administration to approve its general use without prescription, and that is why we are announcing it to the general public rather than merely to the medical profession. We have registered it under the trademark *Paxin,* and we look forward to its prompt approval by the F.D.A. and to its widest possible distribution.

—Mr. Henry, if I understand you correctly, you have developed a drug that will stop violence. Does that mean that we are at the point actually of ending war? Or am I inferring too much?

—No, no, no, I didn't say that. Paxin will suppress only the *subjective* feelings that may lead one to seek release through violent action. As I said, the implications of this are most exciting. But we're certainly not prepared to make a broader claim at this point. Much violence, perhaps most, is committed in cold blood, and wars are still started and conducted by rational men, without passion or anger. What effect Paxin may have at this level remains to be seen. I am hopeful, of course, that it will make a difference, but I must caution you against expecting too much. I repeat, we make no claim for Paxin that goes beyond what I have already said. We *do* say that anyone taking it will have no desire to commit an act of aggression. That, it seems to me, is a lot!

—Mr. Henry, it is so much it seems almost too hard to believe. Because it clearly suggests that some form of the brotherhood of man may be at hand. Could you tell us how extensively the drug has been tested?

—Very. We have been working on it a long time, and we have been testing it in its present form, and in variations, for about a year, on a very large and carefully selected sampling of volunteers and inmates of institutions.

—How big, sir? And did they know what they were being tested for?

—Big enough. We are submitting a complete report on our tests to the F.D.A. No, the participants in the tests did not know what was expected of them, nor did the testers know who was getting Paxin, who was getting another drug, and who was getting a placebo. This was known only to those collating the results. And I should add that very few of our own people knew of the possibilities we were investigating. Our supervising research team operated in maximum secrecy, at my instruction, once these possibilities became apparent.

—Mr. Henry, most of us were surprised not to get a product-information kit when we came here, or even a fact sheet. I assume you'll have something for us on the way out, but meanwhile could you tell us something of the chemical composition of Paxin?

—I'm sorry, gentlemen, but we are not prepared to furnish you such information at this time. It was not an oversight. There are possible legal questions involved. Paxin is in fact a combination of a number of existing drugs. Its effects, however, are not merely the sum of the effects of its individual ingredients. They are unique. As some of you may know, such synergistic effects, in drugs at any rate, tend to be harmful more often than not, and testing them is usually precautionary. One I'm sure you're all familiar with is that

81

of barbiturates in combination with alcohol. Very dangerous. But in this case, the combined effect is not only not dangerous, but certain undesirable side effects associated with some of the individual ingredients disappear in the combination.

—By legal questions, do you mean questions of patentability, since Paxin is made up of existing drugs, or are you referring to the dangers of its individual ingredients taken alone, as you just indicated?

—I'm sorry, but I cannot discuss the reasons for this at this time. It may well be that our lawyers are overcautious in telling us not to reveal the composition of Paxin just yet, but that's what we pay them for. Next question, please. You, madam, over there.

—Mr. Henry, you emphasized that there appear to be no contra-indications, and you implied, I think, that everyone might be better off using it. Would you tell us this. Do you plan to market it for the relief of certain symptoms, like anxiety and depression, or as something for everybody, like vitamins?

—Our present plan, subject to getting the green light from the F.D.A., is to offer Paxin for the symptomatic relief of anxiety, tension, depression, psychosomatic fatigue, and related conditions. But we do anticipate that it will be widely used by people who do not think of themselves as tense or depressed, simply because it will make them feel better. So you are correct in your suggestion that its use will go beyond those who think there is something wrong with them. We will also sell it as an anti-aggressive as soon as we can work out a way of persuading people that they might be happier if they were less hostile, and of teaching them to recognize their own hostility for what it is. This won't be easy, I can tell you.

—Mr. Henry, you have qualified your comments several times with the phrase "subject to F.D.A. approval." Do you have any reason to believe the F.D.A. will withhold approval, or delay it, and if so, why?

—Let me put it this way. There is no reason why the F.D.A. should withhold approval from Paxin. None whatsoever. But we recognize that they will have a problem, in that the effectiveness and applicability of this drug is so far-reaching, so new, and possibly so dramatic, that they are bound to proceed with more than their usual caution in licensing it. This is especially true because we want to offer it as an over-the-counter drug. We have asked for the quickest possible action, but we are prepared to be reasonably patient with the F.D.A.

—What do you mean by "reasonably patient," sir? Do you mean that if the F.D.A. takes what you consider an *un*reasonably long time to approve your drug you will take action against them? Go to court, for instance? Or what?

—I'm afraid you have misconstrued my remark. Nothing could be further from my intentions than sounding as if I were threatening or challenging the F.D.A. or anyone else. I repeat, there is no reason why Paxin should not be promptly approved. If it isn't, we'll cross that bridge when we come to it. . . .

2

—Johnson, you're absolutely sure we have nothing at all from M & P on this drug?

—Positive, Dr. Garrison. We've gone through their entire file of abstracts. There's absolutely nothing there that matches Henry's statement to the press. Every test plan they filed with us is accounted for.

—Well, if you're sure—you're sure. That's all for now, and thanks for getting on it so fast. I may be back to you for another check if we find something else to go on. And thanks again.

—Not at all, Dr. Garrison. You can reach me any time.

—Good. . . . Charlie, what do *you* think is up? What kind of a game is Henry playing? He calls a press conference to announce this wonder drug yesterday. Tells us nothing about it—and it turns out he never has. Says all the data has been sent us—but we don't have a thing.

83

—Well, I've been thinking about it, Bob, and I don't know what to think. I read the transcript of that press conference. He did very well for a man who never had a press conference before. I began to wonder if maybe there's something fishy about the "existing drugs" that go into this Paxin. But that makes no sense. What would he gain by it? A press conference is for publicity. Publicity is for selling. If M & P has brewed up some cockamamie mix we can't let them use, they'll just look like fools and where's the profit? And if the stuff is harmless but just another tranquilizer, we call them on that too, so where do they come out ahead?

—What about you, Ellen? Any ideas?

—No, but I don't see why we should worry about it, Bob. Our job here is to approve or disapprove drugs, not newspaper stories. When we get the data we'll act on it. Until then, this Paxin doesn't exist, as far as I'm concerned.

—I suppose you're right, but I can't say either of you is much help. The newspaper story is a fact of life in itself, and we can't act as if we didn't know about it. The press has been on me since yesterday afternoon, and whatever this Paxin turns out to be, right now I'm the one who feels like a fool for not knowing anything. Well, there's no choice. I'll issue a short statement that says that we have no information as yet and will deal with it when we get it. Right, Ellen?

—I don't see how you can go wrong with the simple truth, Bob.

—Especially now, Bob, while it's still simple. I may be wrong, but I have a hunch Henry is going to send us a can of worms. One more thing. I don't see that our dignity will suffer if we give Henry a call, off the record, to find out when we can expect the data. And anything else we can pick up. I can make the call, instead of you, to keep you out of reach, if you like.

—Yes. Good idea, Charlie. Do that. Any objection, Ellen?

—Not seriously. But if it were up to me I wouldn't do a thing. But I know you can't stand doing nothing.

84

3

—Well, you were right as usual, J.O. Garrison was dying of curiosity. He had Charlie Fodor make the call for him.

—What did you tell him?

—That we'd have the data just as soon as we could get it over. He gave me all kinds of openings to say more. I told him nothing at all.

—Very good. Well, gentlemen, the moment of confrontation approaches. We have only one more very small tactical decision to make. Do we send him our formula by messenger and see him the next day, or do we deliver it in person?

—I've been thinking about it, J.O. I'm afraid of Garrison and his staff having the formula too long before we see him. We don't want a premature leak. Let's deliver it in person.

—Walter?

—I agree with Neil, J.O.

—I see. Well, I've been thinking about it too. I agree about the premature leak. But I don't want to sit there like a supplicant while he goes through the formula either. My decision is this. Send him the formula—eyes-only basis—late tomorrow morning, and set up an appointment for the three of us with him and his two deputies for 2 P.M. No steno or tape recorder, of course. If he stands on ceremony, set up a different time, but see that he doesn't get the formula until three hours earlier. Enough time for him to hit the roof, cool off, and prepare to do us in. Will you take care of it, Neil?

—Consider it done, J.O.

—Incidentally, what kind of press did we get?

—Just what you expected, J.O. Big, but not as big as it should have been. Good-sized stories, generally, but not page one. They're suspicious bastards, as you said.

—Very good. We don't want the publicity too intense just yet. That will come after our confrontation with the F.D.A. I look forward to next week.

4

—Good afternoon, Dr. Garrison. Dr. Levine. Dr. Fodor. You know Walter Kamp of our research division, and this is our public relations director, Neil Silvera.

—How do you do? . . . Public relations is new for you, isn't it, Mr. Henry?

—Only in the formal sense. But now that we have an advertisable product we intend to play the marketing game by the same rules everybody else uses. I look forward to it.

—Well, from what I've read of your first press conference, I think you'll do well. But I hope you weren't serious in expecting us to approve this Paxin. You must have other products in mind, certainly. What I don't understand, though, is why you went through this public charade when you know perfectly well we cannot conceivably license anything like this. I rather hope you'll tell us why.

—I hope *you're* not serious, Dr. Garrison. Of course we expect you to license Paxin. It is a drug of inestimable value, without a single contra-indication to its use. Study our test data. Tell us what's wrong with it. I must say I'm surprised at your attitude. It is arbitrary and unscientific of you to make such a prejudgment.

—Come now, Mr. Henry! You're trying to pull my leg, and I can't for the life of me understand why! You've concocted a mishmash of common tranquilizers, stimulants, antihistamines, antidepressants, antacids, analgesics—have I left anything out?—and topped it off with cannabis and heroin, no less. Quite apart from the heroin, about which nothing has to be said, this is a pharmacological joke. A parody of the so-called multiple-ingredient cold tablets. Except that several of these ingredients *are* contra-indicated to each other, that most of them are marketable only on a prescription basis, that cannabis and heroin are illegal, and that the only immediate effect one could reasonably expect from the concoction is a nervous breakdown.

86

—Are you finished, Dr. Garrison? Very well. You, of all people, surely know that you cannot characterize a compound drug by its ingredients. You see the trees, but not the forest. You assume that the combination will have the same effect as if one were to take each of these ingredients separately. You should know better than that. What goes into Paxin is irrelevant. What it does is all that matters. It is a single drug, not the sum of its parts. And what it does is exactly what I said it does at my press conference, and in more detail in the data you have there. If anything in our test results were wrong, that would be something else. But I warn you there isn't, as you will discover when you check it out. I repeat, never mind what it is. Consider only what it does. It offers an opportunity—to *anybody*—to practice a life-style that is both serene and engaged, calm and alert, sociable and peaceful, to a degree enjoyed today by only a happy few. If you delay its introduction and availability because you lack the imagination to conceive that such a drug is possible, you will become the laughingstock of history, Dr. Garrison.

—Mr. Henry, the description you just gave of these marvelous effects of Paxin sounds very similar to the ways addicts often talk about hashish and heroin. Could it be that you are trying to legalize these drugs in the name of a proprietary medicine, and that all the other ingredients simply act as the inert carrier substances, like sugar?

—I will repeat just once more. Paxin is not heroin or cannabis, or anything else that goes into it. It is Paxin, and it is unique. If you doubt its effect, I suggest you try some yourself. It may convince you more than my words.

—Not a chance, thank you.

—Your loss, Dr. Garrison. What about your colleagues? Dr. Levine? Dr. Fodor?

—If Dr. Garrison has no objection, I'll try a tablet.

—At your own risk, Ellen!

—Oh, Bob. Mr. Henry's drug may be unlicensable—that remains to be seen—but I can't see him trying to poison us.

—Well, now! Thank you for your confidence, Dr. Levine. It's reassuring to know that you don't think I'm a murderer or a dope pusher.

—Dr. Levine was being ironic, Mr. Henry, and meant no offense, as you must know. When I spoke of her taking it at her own risk, I was. . . . Well, let me ask you this. In what ways do the effects of this drug differ from, say the effects of hashish or heroin? Obviously the quanities would be critical, but I mean in general terms.

—I can't answer that myself, especially since I've never tried hashish or heroin, but perhaps Dr. Kamp can help. Walter?

—The effects are quite different, Dr. Garrison. Paxin doesn't create passive dependency; it leads to an active mood. There may be similarities in the euphoria, but the same could be said for alcohol for many people, at least superficially.

—But what about addiction?

—We have no reason to believe that Paxin is especially addictive.

—"Especially!" Now, just what do you mean by that?

—Well, "addictive" is a relative term, Dr. Garrison, as we all know. All drugs that are effective—in making people feel better, in relieving pain, in promoting sleep, in performing some useful function or other—are addictive to some extent. Their addictiveness varies as much with the people using them as with their own inherent characteristics. Now, Paxin is an effective drug, one that makes people feel better, and one that they are conscious of making them feel better. So, in that sense, it would be addictive. But if you're talking about real hard-core addiction—escalating dosage, withdrawal symptoms, and the rest—we have no evidence of it.

—Dr. Kamp, please don't fuzz over the question of physical addiction by generalizing about psychological addiction. Paxin contains heroin, the worst kind of physiologically addictive drug. You claim that the effects of Paxin are unique, and independent of the effects of its components. Are you prepared to prove that

88

heroin somehow loses its addictiveness in this combination?

—Dr. Garrison, I'm not fuzzing anything over. The point is that the distinction between physiological and psychological addiction is itself fuzzy. If you were to ask me if Paxin will create a whole new class of wide-eyed, desperate addicts roaming the streets, ready to do anything for a fix, the answer is a flat no. But I can't say that Paxin is not addictive at all, any more than I could say it about sedatives, tranquilizers, or stimulants. To the extent that Paxin fills a need of the person taking it, he will want to take it again and again, and he will miss it if he can't get it. Like tobacco, for instance. And some people more than others. There isn't any flat answer to this one, Dr. Garrison.

—Dr. Kamp, I find it hard to credit the idea that with all the testing on this concoction you say you've done, and knowing the kind of reaction you were bound to get from us, you have no quantitative data for us on addictiveness.

—Just hold on a bit, Dr. Garrison. Dr. Kamp has plenty of data on the so-called addictiveness. He didn't include it in the package because it was inconclusive. There were no correlations other than the obvious ones he has just described in general terms. In case you missed it, Dr. Kamp stated without qualification that we have no reason to believe that Paxin is especially addictive. You jumped so fast at the "especially" that you overlooked the strength of the statement. And something else. . . .

—Excuse my interruption, Mr. Henry, but if "especially" isn't a qualification, what is?

—You seem to insist on missing the point, Dr. Garrison, that any effective drug—or food, or work habit, or any other aspect of behavior—is addictive to one degree or another. Which I was coming around to discuss, if you'll permit. Your reaction of conventional horror at the possibility of addiction is so unrealistic and out of date that it shocks me, especially coming from one who has taken such a broad view of the stupidity of drug control laws as yourself. Let me take an extreme position, as a devil's advocate, for

89

a moment, and ask you: What is wrong with addiction?

—Is that serious or rhetorical?

—Both. It's serious, but it's also rhetorical, because I'll answer it myself. There's nothing at all wrong with addiction *per se*. When I say "wrong," I mean in social terms, of course. The addict, and I do mean the hard-core heroin addict, is no menace to society, as long as he can get his drug and satisfy his craving. And there's nothing in his addiction that necessarily prevents him from performing some useful function, either. He will lack amibtion, to be sure, at least as a general rule, but that's his problem, not ours. I don't mean we shouldn't try to help him get rid of his addiction, if he really wants to, but it is his right to do whatever he wants to with his body and his personality if it doesn't harm anyone else. Now, the result is not attractive to me or to you, but this is also true of all the other ways in which people surrender to life-styles that do nothing for society except maintain their presences in it, for better or worse. I'll go further than that. The lack of drive and competitiveness that is usually characteristic of addicts makes the world a little easier to live in for the rest of us, it seems to me, and perhaps should even be encouraged in some areas. In any case, the real horrors of addiction are more the by-products of the illegality, the social stigma, and especially the enormous cost of maintaining an addiction under the terms we force on addicts because we don't approve of the way they choose to live. Not the addiction itself.

—Since you insist on going through this conventional libertarian argument, Mr. Henry, I'll play the game with you. Granting any man's *right* to destroy himself with narcotics, the fact is that addiction is not a condition consciously *sought* by adults capable of making a decision to this effect. Addiction is something that *happens* to people, usually youngsters or persons otherwise incompetent to judge the consequences of what they're doing. They are victims, no matter how much you talk about free choice and personal liberty and so on, and if you choose to ignore this you are expressing either gross callousness or a simplism based on lack of experience with addicts. However, you said you would be playing devil's advocate, so I assume you don't really believe all this.

—I'm afraid you've missed the point again, Dr. Garrison. I do believe it, and I was saying obvious things to lead up to some that you may not find so conventional. What is really simplistic is your set of assumptions about what is desirable for society. So addiction "happens" to people? So it does, and so do most of the important events and situations that shape their lives, beginning with the circumstances of their birth. These are the chances we all take, without being asked. I'm simply saying that those who have become drug addicts are not necessarily so much worse off than those of us who are addicted to tobacco, or coffee, or alcohol, or chocolate—at least in the aggregate. Or rather that they wouldn't be if their addictions were recognized as something they were entitled to maintain. Or that their addictions are not necessarily harder on the rest of us than our addiction—yours and mine, too, Dr. Garrison—to the pursuit of power and its perquisites. Or money, or fame, or scholarship, or sex, or anything that someone might set as a goal. But I'm a very conservative devil's advocate, and I'm not arguing *for* drug addiction, just for the proposition that it may not be as qualitatively different from, or worse than, the other addictions that drive us on. And that it would be socially as harmless as an addiction to sleeping pills, ice cream, or fishing, except that we force it to be otherwise.

—Oh, come off it, Mr. Henry. This is nonsense. I agree, as you know, that drug addiction is a medical problem, not a legal one. But I certainly don't accept your straight-faced put-on that it's no more harmful than addiction to coffee, tea, or tobacco. What are you selling—and why? What has all this got to do with the price of eggs, or rather, Paxin? Is this your roundabout way of saying that Paxin *is* addictive, even though not "especially," and that it doesn't matter?

—No, and yes. Paxin is not especially addictive—no matter what you choose to read into the word "especially"—but yes, I do say it wouldn't matter if it were. So far as you are concerned, with your responsibility for licensing new drugs, you have two alternatives, which would remain the same, addictive or no. One, you permit it to be freely sold. Millions of people are then relieved of tensions, anxiety, depression, and aggressiveness. If some of them became what you would call addicted to some degree—no, even if they all did—what would it matter? Paxin would be available and cheap—you could always see to that even if you didn't trust us—and the true dangers of addiction, the side effects caused by illegality, contraband price levels, and so on, would be lacking. No harm done, I insist. Or two, you don't permit it to be sold. Then what? Either we make it legally in other countries, or someone else figures out how to make it illegally here. Either way it goes into distribution channels as a contraband narcotic. No question about this at all, it would happen. High prices, murder, and robbery for the price of a fix; the whole combination of violence, degradation, and corruption that you have now with the true hard drugs. The point is it would come in anyway, but instead of being an enormous force for social serenity, peacefulness, and public happiness, it brings in crime and destruction. Is that what you want? I don't think so, Dr. Garrison. Paxin is not heroin, I repeat, but its legal use may well lead to the elimination of the criminal drug culture and to the introduction of sanity in this whole area. Unless it is proscribed, too, by unimaginative administrative ruling—in which case whatever addictiveness it *may* stimulate in some will be multiplied many times over by the obvious psychological effect of its being forbidden fruit.

—Mr. Henry, this whole discursion of yours puzzles me. You are arguing for the unrestricted licensing of Paxin *as if* it is addictive, while you tell us it really isn't, "especially." Are you perhaps trying to cover for the expectation that it will actually turn out to be more addictive than you now claim?

—Dr. Fodor, my answer may surprise you. It is yes—in a sense. I have no reason to believe it will be more addictive than, say, barbiturates, but for some it may. We will in any case print a clear and unambiguous warning about possible dependency on the package. But what I'm really trying to accomplish with all my talk is to show you how *you* can perform an indisputable public service and stay off the hook at the same time. I am trying to show it to you, not spell it out in detail. The whole area of addictiveness is conjectural. I am showing you that you don't have to fall into the trap of assuming it is either more tangible or more harmful than it is. I am offering you an unprecedented opportunity—to license a drug that provides all the desirable features of so-called addictive narcotics without their ugly concomitant social side effects.

—Charlie, I think we've had more than enough on this. Unless Mr. Henry or Dr. Kamp has something new to say on addictiveness, let's go on to other questions, bearing in mind very carefully what we've already heard. O.K.? . . . Now, gentlemen, are there no other side effects from Paxin? You mention none in your summary here, and you claim no contra-indications. Is this absolute, or are there some "not especially"s here as well?

—None at all, Dr. Garrison. Just that some people die after taking Paxin, though not from the Paxin. It's an interesting effect.

—Come again. Did I hear you correctly? People *die* after taking it?

—Yes. As I said, it's an interesting effect.

—Are you serious, or are you trying to pull our legs again? If it's a sick joke, I for one don't find it funny, Mr. Henry.

—No reason why you should. I was perfectly serious. We have observed during the course of our testing that a small but statistically significant number of people die after using Paxin for a while, more than we might expect from a control group. We find it interesting, and we thought you would too.

—I don't know if I can take any more of your curves, Mr. Henry. You sit there and tell me with a straight face that your new product kills people—and that we should license it for over-the-counter sale. I'm not amused. Perhaps we will now have the privilege of hearing a lecture on the value of Paxin in euthanasia, or population control, or whatever. I assume *this* data is in the package you've given us, along with the rest. If you're serious, which I still doubt, what in God's name leads you to waste our time and your own on this stuff? Or to make pointless jokes, if that's what it is?

—Dr. Garrison, you weren't listening carefully. Of course this data is *not* in the material we submitted. I said that a statistically significant number of deaths ensued among Paxin users, but I also said they didn't die *from* the Paxin. There was no evidence of any kind of cause and effect. We might as well have included data showing that the subjects taking Paxin dressed better after a while, and enjoyed their food more, than the others—they did, you know —but we didn't, because it was secondary. Nobody died of taking Paxin. But a lot of those taking Paxin died, which is not the same thing.

—Oh? How can you be so sure of that? A statistical correlation is *prima facie* evidence.

—Of course, but of what? In this case, merely that more than the expectable number of persons died after using this drug. I can show you similar statistics indicating that more people die after moving from one city to another than a like group not moving— and from causes that can be related to the moving only by the most tortuous reasoning. Should you then try to prevent them from moving, for medical reasons? In this case, you haven't yet asked what these subjects died *from*. So let me tell you anyway. They died from *exactly* the same distribution of causes as the control group fatalities, except in greater numbers. The same proportion of coronaries, cancer, suicide, accident, everything. No traceable cause and effect of any kind.

—What's the order of magnitude, the percentage increase in deaths?

—Walter, suppose you take it from here.

—Yes. It's about 12 per cent, Dr. Garrison, across the board, for a very large sampling.

—What about acceleration? If you have 12 per cent for the period covered—about a year, right?—won't it accumulate enormously after, say, five or ten years? Compound interest principle.

—No, Dr. Garrison, oddly enough. If it did, it would be a pretty formidable population reducer. The figure is good for those taking Paxin for up to five months only. Those taking it longer have exactly the same mortality rate as the control groups. There's no extrapolation. It's a final figure. What it means, statistically, is this. You take anybody's chance of dying in a particular five-month period—which is damned small except for certain obvious groups, like soldiers in battle, or those suffering from a major disease, or the very old—and you add 12 per cent of that small number, and what of it? Our test sampling included these special groups, incidentally, with the same result, 12 per cent higher. But when you compare this really slight increment in risk—far less than the increment in risk of death that you assume automatically when you take a five-hundred-mile trip of any kind—to the enormous gain in the quality of life that Paxin offers, it becomes negligible. As it happens, this gain is most spectacular among those high-risk groups, especially among those who are aware their chances of early death are high. In most cases, it makes this knowledge bearable and their last months or years fruitful.

—Walter, may I put in a word here? I'm not a scientist, Dr. Garrison, just a PR man, so I'm accustomed to being treated with, uh, suspicion by scientists. But I thought you might be as impressed as I was by a fact I know a scientist like Walter wouldn't be likely to mention. It's this. A number of our own people who have been in our Paxin project have been taking Paxin themselves. When they found out about this 12 per cent thing, not one of them stopped taking Paxin. Not one!

—Very interesting, Mr. Silvera, as you say. I could take the edge off your enthusiasm by suggesting some unexciting explanations, but I think that all these subjective observations, including what Dr. Kamp said about the "quality of life" of those expecting to die, are irrelevant. Please don't apologize for your calling, Mr. Silvera. As far as I'm concerned, all three of you are PR men, whatever else you may be. . . . Mr. Henry, I'd like to know how many, and which, of your own people have been taking Paxin, what their functions have been in the testing, and whether they are included in the statistics.

—None were included in our sample figures and none were involved in the testing. But you raised the question of the relevance of what Walter and Neil were saying. That brings us to some fundamentals. I hope you're ready for them.

—What now?

—You seemed shocked, automatically, when I said the Paxin-takers had a slightly higher near-term mortality rate than the controls. You seemed somewhat appeased when Dr. Kamp made it clear that the actuarial difference was so little, net, taken over an average lifetime, that an insurance company wouldn't bother adjusting rates for Paxin users, except possibly for a very short-term policy. We've inquired, incidentally—it isn't just my off-the-cuff opinion. Our insurance company sources agree with us that Paxin will probably lead to *reduced* mortality rates over the long run—it's simple common sense—even though we obviously can't do better than speculate about it for some time. But since we can't prove it—and I can see you're about to point out that x years of Paxin-taking may lead to another period of higher mortality—we'll ignore the probability that the insurance people are willing to bet their hard cash on. I'm even willing to assume what none of us believes, that there may be another period of increased mortality. O.K.?

—Just a minute, Mr. Henry, before you go into what you call fundamentals. Let's try to understand one thing that *I* think is fundamental. You claim, you even guarantee, that there is no cause and effect relationship between Paxin and the five-month 12 per cent mortality increase. Yet you admit there is an indisputable connection. Nothing clean, like Paxin leading to leukemia or suicide, but a definite quantitative relationship. There has to be a reason, and I don't agree that secondary effects necessarily require a tortuous logic. What is it, or what do you think it is? Dr. Kamp?

—We've gone into this with a great many expensive consultants, Dr. Garrison, and not just physicians, physiologists, and psychiatrists. Sociologists, psychoanalysts, and some all-around good thinkers we respect. We have a consensus, Dr. Garrison, which also covers what Mr. Henry said about *lower* mortality in the long run. . . . The use of Paxin, they think—we all think—releases a general complex of artificial tensions, the kind that derive from what we all think of broadly as social conditions. The way we live. These tensions, although they act in the *long* run to speed physiological and mental deterioration, tend to inhibit *short*-term breakdown of functions, by holding some natural entropic processes in check. Releasing them—bringing physiological functions, emotional responses, and intellectual controls back to what we might think of as a more "natural" interrelationship—would tend to liquidate this short-term protection against breakdown. Another crude way of putting it would be to say there are a certain number of people, represented by this 12 per cent increment, who are really ready to die anyway from whatever cause, but whose unnatural internal tensions delay their letting go. This, at least, is a sophisticated consensus of speculation in a fascinating and important field that should be given more systematic study: why some people die and others don't, under what appear to be the same objective conditions. Now, if this hypothesis is true, and we think it is, by and large, subject to experimental proof, the effect of Paxin is precisely opposite that of virtually the entire pharmacopeia in a most fundamental way.

—How so? You claim that Paxin represents the combination of almost everything good that has ever been developed in drugs that affect emotional and psychological states. How *opposite?*

—Just this. Virtually all other drugs lead to the *altering* of some natural physiological process. Paxin, we think, tends to *restore* the human organism to a natural balance between the internal forces extending and intensifying life and the degenerative or suicidal processes leading to death. In other words, it is a drug that returns people to a more natural state, consistent with the limitations of societal demands. You could even call it an anti-drug drug, and you wouldn't be far off, especially if you take into account the unnatural, "drugging" effects of social pressures. We think it offers an enormously exciting prospect—a drug that may in due course bring mankind back to nature in the best sense of the word. Not barbarism, and not giving up the advantages of technological and scientific advance—the "unnatural"—either. A world at peace and in harmony, and yet retaining fundamental human capacities for excitement and emotion——

—For God's sake, Dr. Kamp! Get off that cloud you're riding! Both you and Mr. Henry made a big point that your claims for Paxin were essentially limited to two things: that it made people feel "better," in a variety of ways, and that there were no contra-indications to its use. Then it came out that for all your talk of the irrelevance of the heroin in the mix, it may well be highly addictive, and it now appears to include a considerable short-term mortality factor as well. Now, please! I can appreciate your enthusiasm for what you conceive to be the world-shaking possibilities of this drug of the future, but I must insist you address yourself right now to the question of why the 12 per cent mortality increment it causes —all right, releases, if you prefer—should not bar its use. You have given us vague speculation about the reason for this increment— and that's all it is, no matter how many big names you can produce to support it—and it isn't enough. Your own statistics still defeat you, unless you can show, and *prove,* some social benefit that overrides this mortality increment so clearly that anybody, not just us bureaucrats, will accept it.

—Dr. Garrison, that's exactly what Dr. Kamp was trying to do. His enthusiasm was not merely rhetoric, as you implied. He, and all of us, are more than just wishfully optimistic about the social possibilities of this product. The point we are trying to make is not a contradiction of our cautious statement to the press. We still make no *claim* beyond what we told you. But we are eager to test, and we hope confirm, our belief that much broader claims *can* be made. This can be done only if Paxin is permitted general distribution, not only a test sampling, however large. The point of our rhetoric is that these possibilities are so important that they justify a trivial temporary increment in mortality. My personal opinion about the 12 per cent, which I don't ask you to accept even for the sake of argument, is much stronger than Dr. Kamp's. I think these are people who *should* die, by the morality of natural biological processes, and that this kind of *natural* morality is now beginning to be understood again in our species as it used to be. I mention it only as a reminder to you that public acceptance of this small risk is going to be much less of a problem than you fear. From all the public hoopla about ecology, the environment, and so on, the most important residue is the growing realization, vague as it may be to most people, that the real price of making the world fit to live in is getting rid of the part of the population that makes it more difficult or even impossible. Up to now the emphasis has been on birth control and war, but it will soon become more sophisticated, believe me. Here we have the chance of making a great leap forward in this direction, and I put it to you that people are ready for it.

—On what evidence, Mr. Henry?

—On what I see going on, Dr. Garrison, and you see it too. Where should I start? Perhaps the drug culture would be best because you are close to it. Our little shadow-boxing about addiction was unimportant compared to the general attitude of letting go, of not caring about consequences, that it reflects. It may be an historical irony that this great wave of social recklessness is sweeping over us at a time when concern about public safety—safe foods, safe cars, safe water and air, safe everything—gets more lip service than ever before. But the kids who knowingly risk their lives by taking almost any drug pushed at them are not a separate culture; they are doing what their elders are doing in different ways. Which is accepting a ridiculously high level of risk in their daily lives, not because they really have to, but because of this modern version of social fatalism they have accepted. It's not ignorance. Who, really, doesn't know *how* dangerous smoking is? They keep smoking. We know now that any number of common foods are enormously destructive; most of us will continue to eat and drink them. The same is true of half the accepted routines of living. But we see it most clearly in the callousness that is now the rule about mass killings of any sort, not just war atrocities. People expect them, and they don't care. It's more than just a matter of degree, this change. Now some attribute this to the invention of the bomb, some to technology in general, some to long-range political developments, and others believe the species is in the throes of a great biological process of thinning itself out. Perhaps they all are involved, I don't know. But the phenomenon is real, and you know it.

—Let's keep to the point. How does any of this relate to the acceptance of a risky drug? There are any number of people, I'll agree, who would make a market for a drug guaranteed to kill them in five years if they thought they'd get a kick out of it, but that's not our problem. We are responsible people, and we are responsible to other responsible people. What has this fatalism, alienation, callousness, whatever you want to call it, to do with our decision? You think we should cater to it?

—Not at all. The point is that it affects all of us. You could call it the instinctive underlayment of the more articulate concern about population control that most of us share. It affects us to the extent that although we deplore it, we acknowledge it by not fighting it too hard. Take the present case. You may get some static from the consumer protectors when you license Paxin, if you publicize the 12 per cent increment. But even if you do, it won't be wholehearted. That's the difference the new ambience makes, and why it will come to nothing. You know it. It might not have been true five years ago, but it is now. And you don't have to use this information we've given you, because it's off the record and there's no cause and effect. The fact that our sample was big enough to give mortality figures is unusual, and that we took the time and money to look for correlations of this kind is almost unique. You know as well as I do that any number of your "safe" drugs—in common use, not treatments of last resort—have far higher mortality-increment figures than Paxin, but you don't have a problem about them because no studies have been made and the question hasn't arisen. You *know* this has to be true. The reason we've gone as far as we have is that we don't want to prejudice the chances of a drug as important as Paxin by giving anyone reason to suspect we're not dealing with it as respectfully as it deserves. After it's in general use we'll be able to develop far more sophisticated studies with much larger samples, unless you make it impossible for us by driving Paxin underground. We're at a watershed, Dr. Garrison. I urge you, don't miss the crossing.

—Is that all, Mr. Henry?

• EXPLANATIONS are in order.

First of all, in case you wondered, the entire McCallum and Parker pitch presented by their President Henry and their Dr. Kamp is a fraud. Paxin is a fraud. The statistical data they presented are inventions. The arguments made on the basis of these data are therefore not merely exaggeratedly favorable interpretations of fact but wholly abstract sophistries.

ITEM: No formal testing was actually done on the Paxin at all. Other drugs, with known effects, were used, along with the customary "controls" and placebos. The fact that the testing was rigorously "double blind" made it much easier for Henry, Kamp, and a handful of others to shape and certify all the data submitted. It may seem surprising that a stunt like this could be brought off within the constraints of corporate procedures. What is harder to believe is that a fair-sized group—in this case, twelve persons—of reputable scientists *would* conspire in such a fraud. (Faith in institutions goes deep.) Such a possibility certainly never occurred to Garrison and his colleagues. He suspected a certain amount of corner-cutting, as part of the expectable nucleus of chicanery inherent in free-enterprise business promotion, and he was obviously skeptical of the interpretations proffered by Henry and Kamp. But that the whole package was a giant swindle? Hardly. But once you can bring yourself to consider this alternative seriously it becomes easy to see any number of ways in which the M & P men might have worked it. The unwillingness of most persons even to imagine the possibility that a large group of respected "professionals" or "leaders" could behave in this way is what makes it so easy for governments, for instance, to perpetrate the spectacular lies they think they need to justify—you name it. But that's another subject, or appears to be.

ITEM: Garrison's sarcastic comments about Paxin's multiple ingredients being a cover-up for a type of blended heroin and not much more were, as it happens, right on target. It never occurred to him that his sour witticism could be the literal truth. Kamp's wordplay about addiction and Henry's guarded remarks about "possible" strong addictiveness were merely preliminary defensive steps—the first of many they anticipate—to enable them to extend the use of Paxin until addiction to it is sufficiently widespread to establish it solidly.

ITEM: All the marvelous qualities attributed to Paxin—the "affirmative" feeling of well-being, the tranquilizing effect, the elimination of subjective aggressiveness, etc.—are common among narcotics users. Context is everything, though, isn't it? By glossing over the matters of addiction, dependency, and eventual physical deterioration, Henry makes it sound very good. His and Kamp's frequent use of variations on the word "natural" to describe the quality of life to which Paxin will reintroduce its users is ironical indeed. An equation is implied between naturalness and "letting go," as well as an easy assumption that both must be desirable. Since the most conspicuous stresses of modern life are associated with its most conspicuously "unnatural" activities, the logical jump is made before you know it. Identifying the use of hard drugs with a return to nature of some sort surely exemplifies the old truism that *any* proposition that is boldly asserted and plausibly maintained has at least a fair chance of acceptance.

ITEM: The 12 per cent mortality increment is also an invention, but an important one for its creators. For all their apparent urging to Garrison that it be kept quiet, they know it won't be. They don't want it to be. It is essential, they believe, that a modest, but not negligible, element of risk be attached to getting users started on Paxin, to establish a favorable climate for mass addiction. And publicizing the risk early on will assure them important protection when Paxin addiction is well enough advanced to begin to reveal its far *more* formidable effect on mortality rates. For this, of course, is the name of the game, which brings us to——

ITEM: Their motive. Henry is a population-control nut, not to put too fine a point on it, and he has recruited a like-minded group about him. (It includes Kamp, of course, but not Silvera, who takes the phony addiction line in stride as consistent with standard advertising practice but who doesn't know about the total fakery of the testing or about what is really involved.) He has indicated as much in his speechifying to Garrison, but only in the manner of a man who will use any argument that comes to hand to advance his case, in this instance presumably to promote product and profit. (Henry is not the first, nor will he be the last, to conceal a principled interest by professing a base one.) Much of his argumentation is sincere, to be sure, as when he is trying to persuade Garrison of the degree to which people will accept unreasonable risks, but he has been careful to conceal, despite the clues he has offered *en*

103

passant, the real purpose of Paxin. It is to kill people, as many as possible.

The causes of death will be varied, although hardly consistent with general mortality tables as claimed for his imaginary "mortality increment." Accidents will be number one, followed by overdose, suicide, respiratory paralysis, etc. In Henry's view, those who let themselves become deeply addicted to Paxin will be those most dispensable to society, virtually by definition. The pattern with Paxin will be that of hard drugs in general—dependence, addiction, tolerance, alienation, loss of affect, and eventual death (due "naturally," as Kamp would say).

Henry and his colleagues have no misgivings about assuming moral and practical infallibility, and acting on it. It is perhaps a logical extension of what technologists are already doing, without fanfare, and with no more authority than the print-out of a computer—whose original sin was programed by other technicians, offering distorted alternatives to skewed versions of other problems.

In his own way, Henry is following a path to utopia. He envisages a world that he and his like will manage, using the users (of Paxin and its successors) to do the work, shoulder the risks, and make space for others when no longer productive. Such contempt for mankind is not inconsistent with a spirit of righteousness. Most salesmen are contemptuous of their customers, salesmen of the many and varied brands of happiness most of all.

Finally, will the F.D.A. approve this scheme? They probably will, with hedging, cautionaries, the whole bag of accredited bureaucratic disguises for capitulation. These won't bother Henry and his friends; all they want is a foot in the door.

CHAPTER NINE

1

Washington, May 12—Members of the Joint Congressional Committee on Public Safety will meet tomorrow in closed session to hear testimony on food additives from representatives of the United Foods Corporation.

The closed session, unprecedented in the Committee's short lifetime, was granted at the request of UFC officers. Senator Alexander Corcoran, chairman of the joint House–Senate group, said in a statement to the press that the concession was made "in the interest of expediting the unobstructed exchange of information between the Committee and the company's expert witnesses." He added that "no part of the substance of the testimony elicited from the witnesses that may bear on a legitimate public interest will be withheld from the public," but that the company's "legitimate trade secrets" would be protected.

The Committee's decision to permit a closed session represented a compromise aimed at avoiding a legal showdown, according to informed Congressional observers. Company attorneys had served notice that UFC witnesses would refuse to testify about products not yet offered or proposed for sale in interstate commerce, and would offer no opinions about "intangible" future plans involving products, distribution, and effects.

The principal question at issue, it was said, had to do with the relative safety of a new food preservative the company is planning to introduce to the trade this fall. A story about the product is scheduled to appear in the forthcoming issue of *Digest of the Month,* under the heading of "The Miracle Ingredient That Keeps Food Fresh Forever!"

2

—Senator, we don't have a name for it yet. We call it Formula 30.

—That's good enough. But what's it made of? What goes into it?

—A good many things, Senator, which I don't think it would be helpful for me to read off. I'll give you the list here, though, for you and your staff to examine, but I'd like to remind the Committee at this time, if I may, of our understanding about protecting trade secrets. We have a patent pending, of course, but if a competitor were to lay his hands on this formula it would probably save him many months in developing his own product of this general type. This would be a most unfortunate, unfair, and damaging eventuality, as we agreed yesterday.

—Mr. Anderson, our commitment to this understanding was explicit and doesn't need to be reaffirmed. Obviously we will maintain our end of it in good faith. And obviously it's possible that a leak could develop, even as it might from your own personnel, but we don't anticipate it. Let us proceed, please. Would you please describe how your Formula 30 works?

—Certainly. Or rather let me tell you what it does. Used in recommended proportions, which of course vary widely among different foodstuffs, it inhibits the growth of bacteria, fungi, yeasts, molds, other biological contaminants, oxidation, and other processes of decomposition for what looks, so far, to be an indefinite period. By that I mean we don't yet know what the time limits of its effectiveness are. It is not just another "food preservative." It is a fixative.

—It will preserve any kind of food?

—Almost. In general, it has to be included in the solution or mix the food is cooked in. It will preserve some raw foods, but not most. Its principal applications, we think, will be in cooked and partially cooked meats and fish, in bread and bakery products, in dairy products, and in a wide range of variety foods. There are more, but these look to us like the main ones so far.

—How does it work? Cooked meat keeps pretty well in cans, doesn't it, without putting a new preservative in it?

—Yes, but not after it's been opened. With this fixative it will keep long after, without refrigeration, or with moderate refrigeration, depending on the amount of the formula you use.

—Better than it would if you just dried it out?

—Much. Drying is effective, as far as it goes, but is very limited in application, and, of course, the meat and fish must be *kept* dry, which is not always easy. Formula 30 doesn't affect flavor at all. The food will taste just as good or as bad as it does when it's prepared.

—What about using it in the home?

—Eventually, we think, but not yet. The process is still a little too tricky for the average home kitchen.

—What about bread and milk?

—It will keep bread from getting moldy. It will keep fresh dairy products from going bad.

—Even without refrigeration?

—Yes and no. It's a matter of how much is used, just as with meat and fish. We don't yet know how much more people would pay for milk that requires no refrigeration at all than for milk that simply won't go sour in the refrigerator. But we'll find out soon enough.

—And how do you propose to do that?

—By test-marketing, Senator. We plan to recommend different fixative strengths to different dairies and to suggest to some of the larger ones that they offer two, or even three, levels of keeping quality. Our current guess is that people who already have good

107

refrigeration capacity will elect to keep using it and that the fully preserved dairy products will be preferred in backward areas, where refrigeration is lacking or inadequate. It's merely a matter of merchandising, Senator.

—I see. And what were the other foods you mentioned?

—Variety foods, so-called. Syrups, jellies, jams, catsup, canned soups, what not. For our purpose, any other processed foods that are subject to deterioration. Formula 30 will extend their life after they have been opened at home. This, of course, will be a smaller market.

—What about fruits and vegetables? And what seems more important to me, grains?

—It will work very well on canned fruits and vegetables, and some fresh ones, and we expect this to be another minor market, Senator. Unprocessed grains are a special problem. We are working on a formula related to 30 that we think may offer the same protection to grains, as well as to certain kinds of raw produce, but it's not ready yet. . . . You haven't mentioned eggs. The formula will work well wherever eggs are part of a mix—as in an eggnog, or in a bakery mix, or even in preprocessed scrambled eggs—but it will not work for raw eggs in the shell. Not yet.

—I see. Mr. Anderson, I will now ask you to state what you consider the probable economic impact of this product. In general terms.

—Certainly. Senator, I'm glad you said "in general terms," because we are hesitant about coming up with what may sound like a most sweeping statement. We think that the annual savings against food spoilage, world-wide, that this single product will induce will be in the order of billions of dollars. The Department of Agriculture can give you some figures for this country alone, but their data will necessarily be limited to measurable losses in manufacture, transit, and storage. They will not include the bigger factor of direct losses to the consumer from spoilage at home, which are difficult to estimate. In other words, I think the impact of our product on the world's food supply will be enormous. In view of the so-called Malthusian crunch, the rising ratio of population to food supply, the *political* significance of Formula 30 is obviously of equal potential, although I won't attempt to offer analysis in this area. The importance of this product will far transcend its economic value to our company.

—Which will be considerable, I would think. Perhaps you can give us an idea of your anticipated costs and profits on this product.

—Excuse me, Senator, I don't see how this can be considered a legitimate part of this inquiry. But I will say this. As is customary with new products, we will, quite frankly, set a fairly high initial price for Formula 30 in relation to its cost of production, until we get back our research and development investment. We will then distribute it at the modest profit margins that are characteristic of the food-processing industry. We will not exploit our monopoly position, and we will license other producers on a fair and open basis. The significance of this product is so great that we feel we cannot afford even the appearance of profiteering on it.

—A prudent response, Mr. Anderson. However, what I was leading up to was what the product would cost the meat packer or the baker or the dairyman. And in due course the consumer, which is what I am most interested in.

—I can't give you exact figures, but I assume the order of magnitude is what you want?

—Exactly. Will fully protected meat cost the consumer a penny a pound more, a nickel, a quarter, or nothing at all, or what?

—Well, meats will vary. For effective extension of preservation —that is, an indefinite keeping quality in what our labels describe as a "cool, dry place"—most meats will cost the packer from two to four tenths of a cent per pound. For complete fixation, requiring no refrigeration at all, it would run from about a cent and a half to three cents. For most fish, these figures should be tripled. For bread, depending on type, it would be perhaps a tenth of a cent a pound. For whole, fluid milk, it would run from about a half cent

109

a quart to four cents, again depending on the level of keeping quality desired. Now, these figures are based on our current costs, which will eventually come down. At retail, the consumer may pay about twice these differentials, somewhat more at first. Does this give you want you want to know?

—Yes, Mr. Anderson, for the time being. Would it be a fair statement then that the cost of indefinite preservation would not be a qualitative factor? That is, except for fish and a few other items, the treated food would not be priced up into another class?

—Definitely. The premium the consumer will pay might be comparable, say, to the increase in food prices he gets stuck with every year or two anyway, for which he gets nothing at all in return. But in the big economic picture, Senator, the cost-benefit ratio for the food economy as a whole from this product will be spectacularly favorable.

—Thank you, Mr. Anderson. You have been helpful in giving us a background. My questions may have seemed irrelevant to the issue of public safety, but they weren't; the presumed benefit of a new product has a critical bearing on the standards of safety we feel should apply. To take an extreme example, a medical procedure that entails a 50 per cent risk of death is perfectly acceptable when it is used only on patients who have little reasonable hope of survival. Conversely, we would see no justification for, say, a simple cosmetic that might endanger its user in any way whatever. I needn't labor this analogy. Now, I think we can proceed to——

—Before you begin on safety questions, Senator, may I ask what information this Committee wants from us that we won't provide the Pure Food Administration in any event? Why the duplication? My question is for the record.

—For the record, the mandate of this Committee is to pursue the question of public safety as it affects the quality of life of the American people, in more general terms and with broader criteria than any one regulatory agency can reasonably be charged with establishing and enforcing. It was the judgment of the Congress that the people are rightly concerned by an accelerating trend toward greater incidence of accidents, illnesses, and fatalities resulting from products, services, and public activities that are unsafe, but need not be. Our interest in your new food preservative stems from the continuing discovery that food additives in common use for many years, and thought to be safe, are not safe. In one case after another, it seems, we find that we have been poisoning ourselves, Mr. Anderson, by what we put into our foods as well as by what we dump into our air and water. I don't have to list the most recent shocking examples. Up to now, your industry has not been sufficiently concerned, except under duress. This Committee wants to ensure that the new "advances" in food technology don't turn out to be regressions. . . . Very well. What can you tell us about the safety of Formula 30?

—Actually, very little, Senator. Quite frankly, I don't think we're going to know what the long-range effects of ingesting Formula 30 are, or if there are any at all, until it's been in use for several years. No one had any reason to believe the common preservatives you've just referred to were dangerous when they were introduced. I don't see how we can actually *prove* that Formula 30 is completely harmless at this stage or how anyone can prove that it isn't.

—Mr. Anderson, I appreciate your candor. You're the first witness we've heard from who hasn't begun his testimony by assuring us that whatever he was selling was absolutely, positively safe.

—Thank you.

—Nevertheless, I find it hard to believe that you have no data at all for us, no information about the safety of the product or its ingredients. I know you can't tell us how it will work for twenty years, but you must have run tests on short-term effects, and certainly some on animals.

—Senator, we have no confidence in most animal analogies, and our short-term testing with volunteers has been inconclusive.

—You mean the results don't prove there's a hazard? Or what? Do you mean perhaps that you have nothing to show us because what you have doesn't look good?

—Senator Corcoran, that remark is unwarranted.

—I'm glad to hear it. Please explain how.

—Inconclusive, as I said. We simply cannot say with any certainty that there were or were not any significant side-effects from Formula 30. If we didn't feel we had to lean over backwards to admit to any bad result—contrary to your implication—I could just as well have said there was "no evidence" of any deleterious effects. And all our research people feel that animal tests are inappropriate for a product of this kind.

—Why so?

—Because if there are undesirable effects they would almost certainly affect the brain and, or, the central nervous system. Animal analogies are notoriously unreliable in such cases.

—We'll discuss that with our consultant, Dr. Washington, in due course. The results?

—They were mixed, Senator. Some animals showed evidence of brain changes; most were not perceptibly affected. You must remember that the dosages we used were far heavier, on the basis of proportionate body weight, than would apply to humans. We do this to try to expedite whatever effects might show up over a longer period. Translating time into product concentration may not be a legitimate equation, but we do it because we have no better way of getting around the time problem. But we feel in this case that the whole animal testing business is more likely to be misleading than helpful.

—But you do it.

—Only because it is expected of us, Senator, as your questions prove.

—Granted. Now, will you tell us, in layman's language, what kind of brain changes appeared in these animals?

—Yes. The effect, where there was one—and with enormously multiplied quantities, remember—was to immobilize, so to speak, a number of brain cells. Enough to affect learning performance, memory function, and reaction time, to a small but measurable degree. These results were from rats. But other test animals were not affected, including rhesus monkeys.

—I see. What about your testing on humans? You said it was inconclusive, but could you tell us some of the variations that appeared?

—Well, sir, in most of the test subjects no effect of any kind was apparent. In some, there was the suggestion of possible minor brain dysfunction. In some, there appeared to be an *increase* in learning performance. In general, there was nothing of statistical significance. Of course, we didn't use the heavy overdoses we did with the animals, but we did use several times the amount people could normally ingest if Formula 30 were in general use.

—Mr. Anderson, how can you tell us your studies were inconclusive and in the next breath tell us your product appeared to cause brain damage to "some," whatever number that is?

—Because, Senator, the statistical data, which we'll turn over to Dr. Washington, don't *prove* anything.

—Are you suggesting that the brain damage might have been caused by something else, or was a matter of random chance?

—We just don't know. Senator, let me repeat. We don't believe these tests, or any tests, on this kind of product *prove* anything, and what they may *suggest* in the kind of limited test we can program in advance of general distribution is likely to be misleading in the long run. There are many such examples in the history of food additives. However, the testing we did do was careful and conscientious.

—I'm not questioning the good faith of your company, Mr. Anderson, at least not at this time, but I must tell you I am disturbed by what to a layman are obvious inconsistencies. Now, can you tell me something about these test subjects who, as you say, just possibly might have suffered some small brain damage? Is there any other hypothesis your research people can offer to explain these cases other than the ingestion of your formula? Considering that one class of animals that even I know resembles humans in so many important respects had a bad reaction, it would seem to me there is a strong presumption that nothing further should be done with Formula 30 pending more extensive testing.

—To deal with your last comment first, Senator, I will tell you flatly that unless you do a series of tests that takes the best part of a human generation, perhaps twenty years, you won't get a more definite answer than I've already given you. There is a limit to the degree to which biological testing of complex long-term effects can be predictive. However, on your other question, there are some answers, since we were of course extremely interested in the same point. They won't prove anything, but. . . . For instance. All the subjects who might have suffered some damage were uniformly of inferior mental capacity as we are accustomed to think of it. We used standard performance tests, no I.Q.s or other culturally based criteria. With very few exceptions, these subjects also had some physiological function that was impaired or deteriorating. Usually it was circulatory. On the other hand, a number of subjects of very low intelligence did not seem affected by the product at all—these persons were physiologically normal.

—This is very interesting, Mr. Anderson. How do you account for it? Do you have a theory?

—Yes, but we would call it a speculation rather than dignify it by calling it a theory. It's founded on very dubious assumptions.

—What is this speculation that you're so sure is wrong but, curiously enough, have worked out nevertheless?

—It's the data we feel uncertain about, Senator, not our reasoning. A logical explanation would be simply that the ingestion of Formula 30 might amplify certain neural processes on which brain function depends. If these happen to be in some state of degeneration, the initial effect would be to expedite the degeneration, perhaps bringing it to a stable level their neural circuits could maintain. If there is any truth to this speculation we would still have to determine the exact nature of the process. Carrying the logic further, it would mean that persons whose low mental capacity has its origins in genetic or otherwise "healthy" physiological conditions would not be adversely affected.

—Interesting, Mr. Anderson, although I'm not sure I understand you fully. I don't know whether we should be glad or sorry that your speculation is merely a speculation. If it could be upgraded to a theory, and then proved, think of what we might have. A product that would increase the world's usable food supply and at the same time perform a grading service for people, making it objectively feasible to place them at the level of function for which they would be best suited. Biological engineering, eh? This raises some questions much more interesting than product safety. Or do you think I'm being too fanciful for a responsible legislator, Mr. Anderson? I don't think so. I don't think so. I think I'm merely making a logical extension of *your* speculation. I think that will be enough for now, if no members have questions that can't wait. . . . No? Then I think we should have Dr. Washington's views on Formula 30 and its possible effects before we continue further. If there is no objection, this hearing will be recessed until Thursday morning at ten. We thank you, Mr. Anderson, for your candid testimony so far, and we look forward to seeing you then.

3

To: All members   CONFIDENTIAL
From: Percy Washington
Re: United Foods Corporation's *Formula 30*

Although my staff and I will have a technical report ready for you shortly, a general summary may be helpful in determining your line of questioning to take with Mr. Anderson on Thursday.

1. Contrary to Mr. Anderson's disclaimers, the results of tests performed on nonhuman animals, and on rats especially, with products such as this one, are as legitimate as any other animal test results. It is a fair working presumption that the effects of the product on humans are likely to be similar unless and until large-scale testing with humans, or medical experience, demonstrates otherwise.

2. Likewise, the tentative results of short-term testing with humans, despite its obvious limitations, must also be considered indicative on a *pro tem* basis. In this, the tests performed on human subjects were in fact not extensive enough to warrant more by way of conclusions than Mr. Anderson offered.

3. Apart from the meager test results, we have other reason to believe that the ingredients of Formula 30 are likely to affect brain function under certain circumstances. The technical report will go into this in some detail.

4. The "speculation," as he insisted on calling it, that Mr. Anderson offered as an extrapolation of the possible long-term effects of the product is a good deal more than that. Based on what we know of the effects of the formula's ingredients, and even disregarding UFC's limited testing, Mr. Anderson's theory is the most likely prognosis in sight at this time. My full report will develop this conclusion.

5. In summation, it is my preliminary opinion that the use of Formula 30 in the manner proposed by UFC will cause a small and selective, but continuing and cumulative, kind of brain cell dysfunction in individuals in whom certain degenerative processes are already under way. This should apply to something of the order of 70 to 80 per cent of the portion of the American population in the lowest quartile of "mental capacity" (as defined in the technical report), to about 20 per cent of those in the two middle quartiles and to about 5 per cent of those in the upper quartile. It is extremely probable, though not entirely certain, that where the degeneration of the cell function is hastened by the ingestion of the

ingredients of this formula it will be halted when "mental capacity" has been reduced to a level which the degenerating neural cell activity can sustain. It is also extremely probable, though not entirely certain, that the type of cell damage that Formula 30 can be expected to "amplify," in Mr. Anderson's convenient locution, is reversible; this may be a critical consideration for those conditions for which a medical remedy may later be found and may therefore bear on your course of action. It is equally probable that this "amplifying" effect may indeed lead to an *increase* in "mental capacity" for a small number of individuals in whom the cells affected by the Formula 30 ingredients are not only healthy but carry a potential for further stimulation.

I propose no course of action to you at this time. Normally, our findings set forth in paragraphs (1), (2), and (3) would be more than sufficient to disqualify a product of this kind. But the economic, social, psychological, and political implications of this formula are so great that it may well be your judgment that my summary conclusion in (5) may warrant encouragement of the product on an experimental basis.

4

—Mr. Anderson, I should tell you that Dr. Washington did not go into the questions of *efficacy* of your Formula 30 as a preservative. He finds nothing in your data that he feels would preclude the possibility that your claims in this respect are accurate, so we will tentatively accept your statements at face value pending confirmation.

—Very good, Senator.

—Now, let's get down to *our* business. To save time, I will tell you at once that our technical consultant finds no merit in your claim that animal tests are irrelevant in predicting the possible side effects of a product of this kind. He also tells us that even without tests some kind of brain cell dysfunction could reasonably be expected from the ingredients that go into your Formula 30. He also tells us that your speculative prognosis, as you called it so disparagingly, of the effects of your product on a regular user, is entirely plausible, and, on the basis of the limited knowledge of neural processes, even probable. Now, would you tell us why *any* government body, even an investigating committee, should protect a product that we suspect, and you will not deny, may cause measurable brain damage to perhaps 30 per cent of our population?

—You don't fool around, do you, Senator? Very well. Let me say for the record that we don't agree with your consultant's findings in the form stated. . . . Now, as you yourself put it so succinctly when I testified earlier, the entire question of public safety is relative. Acceptability of risk, criteria of side effects, and so on, must all be measured against the potential social gains of the product or service or process under consideration. Although we all understand this, it's terribly easy to lose sight of it when one hears such terrifying phrases as "brain damage," a kind of affliction that stirs up profound unconscious fears in all of us. It is somehow more frightening than most of the side effects you are accustomed to dealing with.

—If you intend to psychoanalyze this Committee, Mr. Anderson, please save your breath and our time.

—If you like. But it's true. Nevertheless, I must remind you that this fearsome-sounding possibility—brain damage!—is limited in several substantial ways. First, it is a possibility, and only a possibility. Second, even if it were a fact, the extent of the damage, as your consultant surely advised you, would be self-limiting and in no case great. Third, since you used the educated figure of 30 per cent as the possible limit of the affected population, you must also have been advised that this group lies overwhelmingly among the least mentally capable. I will discuss other implications of this later. Fourth, if the brain cell effect does in fact exist, you must know that it is equally probable that it will be *beneficial* to a substantial minority of those affected. Fifth, you must also know that if in fact the effect exists it would be reversible. So what does all this horrendous brain damage add up to?

—Just a minute, Mr. Anderson. You assume we know a number of things we haven't mentioned to you. You are right, as it happens. But why are you only *now* getting around to acknowledging them yourself—after you have reason to believe *we* know about them?

—Because, as I testified earlier, we do not accept the entire grouping of presumed effects as probabilities, good *or* bad.

—Please continue.

—As I was about to say, all this hypothetical risk adds up to is this: The general use of Formula 30 *might* cause a reduction of mental capacity among those who are already subject to the abnormal, perhaps even pathological, stress of operating at an intellectual tempo beyond the current capacity of their central nervous systems. It might reduce this capacity—for these same people only —to the precise level at which they are prepared to function healthily. I put it to you, before I continue with the other half of my argument, would these effects be bad?

—In my opinion, anything that may distort the quality of consciousness of any human being without his fully understanding consent is bad. However, I, and all of us, I'm sure, would reserve a serious answer to your hypothetical question until we had more confidence in the self-limiting and reversible characteristics of the effect we're discussing—not to mention a clearer notion of what you think of as a "slight," "small," or a "not great" effect. Please continue.

—I can say with assurance, gentlemen, that if the brain cell effect does take place, it *will* be self-limiting and reversible. I can't define "small" in a quantitative way, but I use the word with confidence, and not for rhetorical purposes. For this reason: The presumed effect would take place only among persons forced to maintain their mental processes at a tempo faster than their neural controllers, which anticipate degenerative effects, want them to. The analogy is coarse, but not inaccurate. It seems logical, from what we know of these processes, that this overload cannot be too "big" anyway, or one of several kinds of mental breakdown would take place. Do you agree, Dr. Washington?

—As being the greater probability, yes, I would.

—Thank you. What I will now say, not by way of making a claim, but suggesting only the possibility, is that the brain-cell-detent effect, as I would call it, would be essentially therapeutic.

—Hold on, Mr. Anderson. You suggest that brain damage can be *good* for you? That's something new!

—It's an easy joke, Senator, but you must know there are no end of medical analogies. Fever and pain have necessary and useful functions, and any number of drugs work by reducing or suspending the activity level—the productivity, the efficiency, or the gross function—of a gland, an organ, the musculature, or what have you. I'm merely suggesting that this possibility is not far-fetched. What makes it seem ridiculous to you, Senator, is that we are talking about something as psychologically delicate as the subject of brain cells. It's like sex. If we were talking about heart function, it would be easier to be objective about it, don't you agree?

—Go on.

—That's all I'm going to say about the so-called dangers of the product, for now. Let's get back to the other side of the balance. What is the context? Gentlemen, I put it to you that even if the risks we've been talking about were real and proved, had no self-limiting factors, were not reversible, and so on, they would still be worth taking. First, I have had our economists prepare several estimates that bear on the general social importance of this product. I will give you each a set of these estimates and ask you to keep them confidential. They deal with the consequences of the general use of Formula 30 on the world's food supply, broken down by areas. They are conservative. Depending on the level of usage you choose to apply, you will see that this product can increase the usable food supply by a factor of from 5 to 20 per cent. The implications are so enormous, in terms of political stability, lives preserved that would otherwise perish, that anything I might say in argument would be anticlimactic. Whether you describe the current world crisis as one of overpopulation, maldistribution, environmental destruction, or inadequate food supply, we have a product that will buy time in which the next generation will at least have the chance to rectify the mistakes of their predecessors. Which is more than the most sophisticated among them have expected. This *is* what our product will do. And this is the context in which you have to consider interfering with its development because a few million of our comparatively retarded fellow-citizens *may* be set back occupationally from jobs that are basically over their heads in the first place to those they can handle competently and without undue stress. That's what it's all about. I will only add that my continuing awareness of this larger context is what may have given you the impression that I have been overcasual about the safety issues that engage your Committee. We are not unconcerned, but the cost-benefit scales are so unevenly weighted that the rest seems like hair-splitting.

—Very eloquent, Mr. Anderson. But it is predicated on confirming both the effectiveness of your product, and the proposition that these dangers are of as low an order of magnitude as you make them sound. . . . One more question. Supposing, Mr. Anderson, that your product has been in general use for a year or so, and supposing that the maximum brain cell damage theoretically possible actually takes place. What will be the tangible evidence? What will the victims notice about themselves? What will be the public effect?

—That's a tough one, but I'll do the best I can. There wouldn't be a conspicuous change. Most people who would be affected— hypothetically!—would be unaware of any difference in the way they behaved or performed. The most tangible indicator would be occupational. Decisions, especially on routine jobs, would be made more slowly and, we think, more accurately. If the inconclusive

121

testing we have done turns out to be predictive, despite our reservations, the reduction in speed of learning and reaction time would be accompanied by a reduction in stress. In general, such effects would tend to be unnoticed by the individual concerned. They would be self-controlling, in the sense that neural systems would automatically set themselves a slower pace. A driver, for instance, who has depended on a certain reaction time will adjust his driving, without being aware of it, to the new neural speed, just as he would automatically allow a lower-powered car more time for passing on the highway. The same would be true for the memory function, which I think any of us who are middle-aged can understand readily. As we tend to forget more details we simply depend more on notes and memoranda, and we live with it without feeling that we cannot function adequately.

—If the evidence will be so intangible, how would anybody know there has been any change at all?

—Through objective criteria, Senator. Tests, production output, anything measurable that is a function of how rapidly and accurately people learn, remember, and respond. An assembly line, for example, might have to be slowed down, while at the same time the accuracy of the work would increase, probably to the extent of providing a net gain in efficiency.

—Continuing to assume your product has this brain-cell-detent effect, as you called it, is there any reason to believe that the general quality of life will be visibly affected? I'm going beyond your assembly-line example. If your people have speculated as far as they have about the longer-reaching aspects of your product, surely they have visualized some kind of social expression of the appearance of the brain cell effect, whatever skepticism about its existence they officially declare.

—More speculation, Senator. Yes, we have. If the effect exists, we would expect it to accentuate and clarify class differences, on an intellectual basis. Those whose mental limitations are the result of a degenerative process rather than innate would tend to cluster at a certain position in the intelligence-distribution curve, which would cease being bell-shaped. Do you follow me? It would have two humps—a large one near the lower end of the curve and a smaller one near the upper end. Inequalities would be recognized as a natural fact of social life, and without stigma. We think that such a stratification would make it much simpler for our society to adjust to new technologies, which will increasingly demand, quite frankly, two general classes of citizens: those who program the machines and those who service them. This brain-cell-detent, if it exists, would be satisfyingly synchronous with the demands of society, as we see it.

I am not trying to persuade you to adopt some new and cynical value system. I am only suggesting that even the relatively small, and unproved, part of the consequences of introducing Formula 30 into our way of life that you think of as being on the negative side of the cost-benefit scale may not belong there at all. Whereas the direct benefits would be, *will* be, entirely unambiguous.

—Thank you, Mr. Anderson. We will take your testimony under advisement. We will get in touch with you if we want further clarification. Before we adjourn, however, I have still one more question, suggested by Dr. Washington. Would the hypothetical effect have any bearing on birth rates, death rates, or other medical pathology?

—Yes. We would anticipate that it would have no net effect on the birth rate but would raise the death rate slightly and selectively. Premature deaths due directly or indirectly to excessive emotional stress would decline, but the suicide rate would go up—almost entirely among the unproductive segments of society, however. I'll mail you our data on it. Also speculative, of course!

5

Washington, May 16—Two closed sessions of the Joint Congressional Committee on Public Safety were evaluated today as "satisfactory" by Senator Alexander Corcoran, chairman of the group. The sole witness, he said, was John Anderson, executive vice-president of United Foods Corporation, who was called to testify on the safety aspects of a new food additive the company is said to have developed recently.

Although Senator Corcoran would not comment on what went on at the closed meetings, he indicated that the group had no immediate plans for hearing further testimony on the UFC product. He said that the Committee's recommendations would be forwarded directly to the Pure Food Administration.

Company officers were not available for comment at this time.

6

Chicago, May 17—United Foods Corporation announced today plans for the distribution of a new food preservative that company officials claimed would "revolutionize" food distribution methods within the next few years.

The product, to be known as Perma-Fresh, was the subject of a secret controversy in Washington recently, which resulted in the appearance in closed sessions of a top UFC officer before the Joint Congressional Committee on Public Safety. The company indicated that it intends to begin distribution of the product in August in selected test markets, pending clearance by the Pure Food Administration.

UFC board chairman and chief executive officer Arthur Payne revealed that test-marketing of the new product has already been under way for some months in several unnamed countries in Asia. Mr. Payne declared that the results of the initial testing were so promising that contingency plans for building additional production facilities abroad were being rushed into execution.

The new product, he said, would be made available to all food processors in the United States as soon as possible. The company is not prepared to estimate how soon the product would be available for home use, he said, but tests of the direct consumer market will soon be started abroad in limited areas.

Mr. Payne also revealed that the company has been engaged in negotiations with the United Nations Food and Agriculture Organization, with a view to obtaining U.N. assistance in expediting use of the product in countries subject to chronic food shortages. He described the discussion as "encouraging, fruitful, and exciting." FAO officials confirmed the negotiations, but would not comment on them.

• THE Joint Committee has heard a plausible expression of concern about the world's food supply and a less plausible concern about those who would presumably be better off by having their intellectual capacities attenuated. Despite the testimony offered, it will not interfere with the marketing of the new additive. The Pure Food Administration will give its customary "interim" approval, by default. If this strains credibility, consider the following.

The P.F.A., although aware that a serious question of safety had been raised, operates on the basis that a product offered by an established manufacturer must be given the benefit of any doubt. Public protection agencies are responsive to the interests of the institutions they are supposed to regulate. Good faith is the initial presumption, and in this instance no *affirmative* case has been made of possibly deleterious side effects. In addition, the P.F.A.'s confidence has been decisively strengthened by the uncontradicted success of the product in other "unnamed countries," and by the public display of interest by the U.N. Nothing is as persuasive as a *fait accompli.* The agency's reluctance to interfere has been reinforced by the failure of the Joint Committee to hoist a warning flag,

125

and even by such irrelevant trivia as the banality of the name chosen for the product. (How could anything called "Perma-Fresh" do anything significant, good *or* bad?)

Corcoran and his Committee, though honestly committed to their role as public defenders, operate on a different dynamic. They have been infected by the temptation to buy drastic remedies, to play God at bargain rates; the prospect of engaging indirectly in a kind of biological engineering, without being responsible for it, is exciting. After all, the "dangers" were speculative, the pseudo-scientific jargon sounded plausible, the witness seemed candid, and the grandiose cost-benefit rationale was no less tenable—to them —than the hypotheses about the brain-cell effects. They took their cue from Anderson, and Dr. Washington gave them an easy out. Besides, if they were to make difficulties for UFC they would have to take affirmative action themselves, in an area in which they feel no professional competence, exposing themselves to a political danger of making fools of themselves. Finally, the responsibility for such action is theirs only at the level of political rhetoric; evaluations of products and explicit decisions are under the jurisdiction of the P.F.A. The Committee has nothing to lose by doing nothing and can pass the buck in good conscience.

Anderson and UFC are motivated only by traditional profit-seeking; no ideologues here. They have persuaded themselves that the product's side effects will be beneficial to society—at least to their part of it—but they know they are exaggerating its efficacy as a food-saver. Although the product will in fact have great commercial value, UFC's representations that it would effect a "conservative" saving of 5 to 20 per cent of the world's food supply must have been calculated on the computer of the same advertising agency that planted the *Digest* article. It will not "revolutionize" anything. More important, the principal food spoilage problem in the countries where shortages are most critical is that of grains, which the new miracle additive will not help. These are also the guinea-pig countries, where products can be tested or merchan-

126

dised without inconvenient restriction—whether Perma-Fresh in Asia, birth-control pills in Latin America, or Chloromycetin almost anywhere outside the United States. Or, of course, new weapons systems.

For all the hedging about those brain-cell effects ("detent," "dysfunction")—which are real, noticeable, and not at all speculative —the more dramatic effect of this supposed great new technological boon to the human race will be one barely touched on at the end of Anderson's second appearance. It kills. This is once more the name of the game. For all the cant about the happy, unstressful lot of those it will reduce to their presumably comfortable, natural levels, the other side of the picture will reveal those who don't adjust to their new serenity. These will be the suicides, in the millions—which the new engineers will justify, sooner or later, as eugenic.

Those who will be killed by the new cars and by Paxin will at least have been given some kind of warning, however disingenuous. The victims of the new food additive will be afforded no such courtesy; their sacrifice will be involuntary. They will be, by and large, the common people of the poor countries and the poor people of the rich ones.

AT this point in the story private initiative gives way to public policy.

PART THREE

CHAPTER TEN

1

Washington, Oct. 1—The Special Commission on National Priorities will hold its first meeting tomorrow, it was learned here today from White House sources. It has been convened by its chairman, Dr. William Francis Rooney, and will meet at the White House Annex.

According to Dr. Rooney, formerly the President's special adviser on environmental affairs, the Commission will operate without fanfare. "When we have something worth reporting, we'll issue a report," he told newsmen. "Until then, don't expect any portentous manifestoes. And just because nearly everything that happens has some bearing on national priorities doesn't mean we have to pass judgment on it. Don't call us, we'll call you."

Of the six associate members named to the Commission by the President last week along with Dr. Rooney, only two are government officials. They are White House assistant Henry S. Harrison, known here as the President's "expediter," who is responsible for liaison with executive departments and agencies, and R. William McGee, Deputy Director of the Office of Planning. They will continue in their present posts, although Dr. Rooney will devote all his time to the activities of the new Commission.

The Commission's other members are: Samuel M. Gold, of the Program Analysis and Development Corporation,

131

of Washington; Lewis Parker, Director of the Institute for Conflict Resolution, of Baltimore; William Spaatz, fellow of the Richardson Institute for Biological Research, of Houston; and Dr. Noble O. Wilson, Director of the National Organization for the Advancement of Public Health, of New York.

2

—Gentlemen, I'm glad to see the class is on time this morning. It's a good sign, I think, and a good start. Sit down anywhere around the table—we all know each other, we can do without protocol. I intend to run our meetings without any red tape or minutes, so whatever you have to say, don't worry about how it might look on paper to somebody else, because nobody else will see anything. And we'll have no comments to the press about anything. If we're lucky, they'll forget we exist.

—I want you first to meet Arthur Smith, who will be our executive secretary, or anything else you might prefer to call him. He knows who all of you are, of course, so we can skip introductions. He will be our *entire* staff, as a matter of fact; I see no need for cluttering ourselves up with more files and paper. Mr. Smith is a systems analyst who has been doing some very, very special work as a consultant this last year or so that I think will make him uniquely helpful to our project. He also has that passion for anonymity that President Roosevelt valued so highly, as do I. That will be enough about him. Except—and this is important—to say that he has my total confidence, and I ask you to keep that in mind when you have anything to tell me when I'm not around. He'll be available.

—Frank, I like the idea of running this commission without red tape, as you know. Absolutely. But don't we have to have some kind of record? A record *for* the record, I mean. When we meet, a summary of actions taken, and so on. If you have to testify before a Congressional committee, for instance. I'm a little concerned that we protect ourselves on procedure.

—Absolutely, Henry. We *will* have a short summary of each meeting, which will record the topics discussed, our conclusions, and whatever ongoing assignments we make.

—But Frank, what the hell! I thought you said no minutes. How can we talk freely?

—Very simple, Henry. I have already dictated the summaries of our first six meetings in advance. Only the dates and the absentees have been left open. These are for the record. If you ever have occasion to need to know what's in them, call Mr. Smith. I'm also preparing a number of reports, or position papers, on a variety of plausible problems, that we can issue if it seems advisable to do so. Air pollution, transportation, and so on. It all comes out of my files from my old job in Environmental Affairs. And very good, too, if I may say so. I have enough ready now, before we start, to get us an efficiency award from any congressman who tries to bug us, Henry. We're prepared, fellow boy scouts. Well?

—Very neat, Frank, as we know we can expect from you. But you might as well level with us all the way. Have you prepared our *real* decisions in advance too? Because if you have, count me out.

—Take it easy, Will. You ought to know my style by now—lots of noise, but underneath it all a humble, modest, cooperative good fellow, right? No, Will, I don't have more than a general notion of what we're going to decide. I will call our meetings and set our agenda and maintain some kind of order, in my usual democratic, high-handed manner, but that's all. Frankly, if I didn't know I needed you—all of you—I would have handled this assignment on my own, instead of persuading the President to make a commission out of us.

—What agenda have you lined up for us now?

—*Now* you're talking, Will. Very well. I *will* exercise my prerogative as chairman to state our problem as I see it, and from there we'll go where our discussion takes us. O.K.? You all know

133

why you're here, because I've talked to you individually, but I think it would be a good idea if I ran through the story again. Mainly to get synchronized, because I didn't tell any one of you *exactly* the same things. Sit back, please.

Our presence here this morning is predicated on the fact that our institutions are breaking down faster than we can patch them up. Right? And by institutions I mean more than the word usually implies. Off on one side I'm talking about political institutions, social and family relationships, the processes of law, education, the arts, public morality, all that jazz. Put it all together and it spells social contract, the way people have to live together to survive. It's disintegrating, and nothing we've been able to do about it so far seems to do any good. The irony of it, if it is an irony, is that as our technology gets more complex we become more dependent on our social contract than we ever were—while at the same time the growth of technology itself contributes to its breakdown, or seems to. Now, off in another direction we have the institutions of physical and economic organization. Public health, housing, and schools; urban development, transportation, communications, and other public utilities; employment, adequate income, and equitable taxation—you name it, everything we're doing now on a crash basis is too late. We just can't make up for the old delays in starting to do something about them, even though we pretend to. Total chaos is damned close—we've had enough signals, as we all know. Then, still further off on the same side is the group of so-called environmental problems—air, water, noise, garbage, overcrowding, radiation, even the threat of nuclear war can be included here. We're not keeping up with them either, in spite of all the noise *I've* been making, and in spite of the fact that we've sold the public a bill of goods that we're on the way. Why shouldn't they think so? —they've spent enough. Anyway, the sense I want to get across to you a little differently from the way I've talked to you about it privately is that we have reached the point where really drastic solutions—unspeakable solutions—are by now, thanks to our social incompetence over the last few decades, the only solutions. Right?

Now, almost everybody, not just us, agrees to this in general terms, and it's even been fashionable to talk this way for some time. It embarrasses me to feel I should go through the list again. But most people—and this includes some pretty sharp cookies—think of drastic solutions as something along the lines of abolishing internal combustion engines, limiting the consumption of power, overhauling the judicial process, penalizing population growth, substantially socializing the economy, and the like. All very well, of course, and necessary. Actually, I think we know by now pretty much what has to be done in the *long* run to prevent the breakdown from becoming irreversible, regardless of our various notions of what kind of society we want to look forward to—which in the last analysis may not be so different or so critical.

But the acute problem is really one of time, compounded by politics. On the evidence of the last few years—during which there has been more public and *serious* recognition of the possibility that our society, and the species itself, may not survive than we know of in previous recorded history—it seems clear that the people, our constituents, our fellow victims, will simply not be ready to accept the measures necessary for survival until we are firmly past the point of no return. It's not really their fault. We have preached the doctrine of automatic progress for so long that we're stuck with it. Our sins have caught up with us.

There are some, I know, who attribute our predicament not to our collective social incompetence but to some fundamental biological inadequacy of the species—presumably now arriving at a point of extinction as genetically inevitable as that of the dinosaurs. They may be right. But we must reject this view as a working premise, and not only because it is unprovable. It is defeatist, hopeless, and dishonorable. Anyone who accepts his stay on the planet with due respect and gratitude has a moral obligation, I say, to *try* to maintain our collective immortality as long as there is an imaginable chance of success. Especially, I put it to you, when mankind has reached the point where it is *also* imaginable that the quality of life for most of the world's people might be improved by a true quantum jump.

So the only immediate solution that we see is to buy time, in the hope of keeping the possibilities of survival open until the body politic is really ready to make the sacrifices it will have to make sooner or later. And those of us here—and fortunately the President as well—agree that the only practical way to do this is to reduce the scope of the problems that aggravate our difficulties.

Now, in fairly plain English, which we must eschew at all costs in anything we communicate publicly, this means that we must reduce—significantly—the numbers of people who contribute disproportionately to the intensification of both our particular and our more general breakdowns. In still plainer English, kill them off. Not casually, not indiscriminately, but purposefully. And not because we are monsters who lack feeling for others, or because we harbor some wishful primordial aristocratic idea that we are more "deserving" or "worthy" of survival than others. And not, by any means, because we assume ourselves to be better qualified than anyone else to pass final judgments of this magnitude. Not at all. *We* will make these judgments because we are among the very, very few who recognize that they must be made, who are willing to assume the responsibility for making them, and who are, incidentally, as "qualified" as we need to be, no more. Which is to say, we are ready, willing, and able.

We will be doing, on a vastly larger scale, what others do, in one way or other, every day anyway. And for a far greater purpose. The best working model for our mission is the triage officer in a military field hospital. He is the doctor who must decide on the disposition of casualties as they come in from the battlefield faster than they can be taken care of. The triage determines who will be selected for immediate medical treatment, who will be put off till later, and who will be abandoned to die. The choice must be made, whatever the criteria. Leaving it to chance—God's will, the presumed fairness of an honest lottery, whatever you want to call it—is not an expression of moral modesty; it is criminal negligence. To waste resources on the hopeless or near-hopeless case while another bleeds to death unnecessarily because he arrived a minute later, or whatever, is absurd. Expand this to the social scale.

The object of triage is simply to save as many as can be saved, and that is the first part of our object. Our criteria will vary as we work them out, but they will surely relate first of all to survival, over the long haul, of the greatest number of *fully functioning and productive* members of the species. Any questions at this point?

3

3 Oct
To: WFR
From: HSH
Re: X. Destroy after reading!

Dear Frank:

I'm *quite* uneasy about sending you written memos. However, Smith insisted that that's the way you want it, that there is no risk, and that you feel it's more important that we get into a freer mood about our business as soon as we can. You said Smith would be your alter ego in this commission—so be it. But you'll understand why what I say will sound a little circuitous.

I'll get right to the point of what's bothering me at the moment. One thing left very much up in the air at our first discussion, it seemed to me, was the matter of scope. I don't have any sense of how broadly we'll be operating, how freely we're being funded, and so on. Will we be able to carry out, as well as decide on, programs that will in themselves alter the conditions of the environment? That is, will we ourselves dispose of large numbers of, shall we say, contributors to our problems? Or will our job be essentially programmatic? Or will we perhaps put into effect some *exemplary* projects? Although you talked as if we would be taking on the whole job ourselves, it wasn't quite clear to me. If we are to carry out these projects ourselves—physically—how will we handle it? Staff? Subcontract? Or what? Knowing you as I do, I know you can clarify this for me quickly, because I know you always have an explicit vision of what is to be done.

What you tell me about what's lined up on the operational side has a bearing on my next suggestion. Although any liquidation of "problems" has to be massive to mean anything at all, I would think that we should begin with one that is limited, until we get accustomed to working together, in respect to size, economic impact, and number of persons directly affected or involved. For a starter, what would you think of a kind of recap of that gas explosion in Chicago last spring? The difference would be the difference between planning and chance. This time there would be a careful comparative cost-benefit analysis of several likely regions, with the choice made rationally. Although, I must admit, the Chicago accident was so well placed, curiously enough, that it might make a planner despair of proving his indispensability. What think? Perhaps you have a better idea. In any case, I think some limited, closed-end project is in order for the immediate future. Obviously, we have to do a thorough job of quantitative and chronological analysis of general priorities, but I think it's important to establish a precedent of action. I don't have to go into my song and dance with you, of all people, about the dangers of overplanning as a *substitute* for action.

Please answer soonest. And confirm this written memo procedure, please. I think better in writing than in talking, as I suppose most of us do, but I'm still uneasy.

Best

Henry

4

Henry, baby:

Relax. Don't be afraid to put it in writing. Euphemize all you please if it will make you more comfortable, but we have to stop this secret-agent whispering style I noticed after our first meeting before it takes root. I am sending out a memo on this (a memo on memo-sending?) to all hands. Naturally the rule will be destroy after reading, but we have to loosen up. Or we'll go crazy, right? And we can't waste time waiting around for each other to be free for private talk. Relax and write.

On operations. This is really what Smith is for. He has his operating people everywhere; you will be surprised to know that he and his associates have been working in this same field, for private (but legitimate!) clients. An unbelievably first-rate man. All you (we) will ever know about operations is what Smith tells us, which won't be who and where, but how much, how many, how long, comparative difficulties, and special problems. Do you really want to know more? I don't think so. We have to trust each other, Henry, in a big way. Trust me on Smith and operations, O.K.?

I'm delighted to see that your good old hard nose hasn't puttied out now that we're in business. I mean your attitude about getting started with action before we get around to making our program complete and precise. I couldn't agree more. I have another program in mind for a starter—also limited, but not completely closed-end (if you mean what I think you mean). Mine concerns tax receipts—comparatively modest, specific objective, results fully quantifiable in terms of benefit (there won't be many like this), easy to execute, minimum natural publicity. Let's kick them both around at the next session, along with any other starters from our friends. As of now, I like mine better than yours, but you may persuade me otherwise.

Finally, on scope. I meant exactly what you thought I meant at the meeting. Scope will be large, funds will be ample, and I have made all the necessary cover arrangements. Essentially, we will plan and we will decide and we will order operations. What we decide, especially in regard to order and timing, will of course be influenced by Smith's feasibility report, which will be furnished by his outside group promptly for each proposed operation. This will include cost and other factors, and may even urge a veto from time to time when he thinks the operation won't work well. *What* we decide, before you jump down my throat, will also be governed by many other considerations. With the kind of all-around expertise we have between us, in all immodesty, I will be astonished if we run into any serious disagreements on feasibility. But, I repeat, the decisions will be ours, regardless of Smith's report, and they will include all the operational decisions needed to implement our policy decisions. There's language for you, Henry. Decisions, decisions, decisions. But I'm not really joking. They will be real and they will be fantastically big.

Keep cool
Frank

5

3 Oct
To: RWMcG
From: WFR
Re: Project One

Dear Will:

There seems to be a general feeling that we should get going on some specific, but limited, project as soon as possible, to avoid

140

catching a case of committee-itis. Something for real, not busy-work, but not exceptionally ambitious. Henry has one idea for this, I have another. Since I will probably carry the day for my own proposal with my usual overwhelming cunning in argument, and since you are suspicious (you said, didn't you?) that I have every-thing set up for rubber-stamping, perhaps I can prevail upon you to give this matter some thought. For the next meeting, O.K.? I don't mean to divert attention from developing our full priority weighting list, but you know the danger of not starting operations as soon as possible.

Yours—

Frank

P.S. Don't be reluctant to send written memos at will, Will, but the rule must be destroy-immediately-after-reading, and no copies.

6

3 Oct
To: WS
From: WFR
Re: Priorities

Dear Bill:

Well, what is it, the chicken or the egg? (I just said that so that you biologists can relax in my ignorance in your field, as of now. Don't count on it forever, though.) What I mean is that although the weighted-priority project must be weighed in as first priority, natch, there is some feeling that we should get started with an exemplary project right away. Reason: It's important that we get a sense of what an actual operation in our area is like, and soon, so that our priority listing will reflect a more realistic sense of what we can and can't get away with.

So I plan to talk about some possible eggs (chickens?) at our next session and would appreciate hearing some of your ideas about omelets.

Best

Frank

P.S. Incidentally, Bill, please make an indelible note in your mind that all memos between us (all eight, incl. Smith) *must* be destroyed as soon as read. *Must.* And no copies.

7

3 Oct
To: SMG
From: WFR
Re: Operations

Dear Sam:

I don't think you have to worry too much that we'll get hung up in what you called "meaningless moralizing" at our meeting the other day. The study of actual priorities—values, comparative effects, the whole bit—*has* to be made, but it doesn't have to hold up the working out of operational plans. As I told you after the meeting, Smith will handle the entire operational side of our work. That's his real job. He and his own people—whom we won't meet —will bring in operational evaluations of everything that goes on our agenda. What we decide will require other criteria as well— all right, *call* it meaningless moralizing or whatever you want, but it's important that we have no doubts at all about the accuracy of Smith's figures. That's why you're so important to us, Sam, as our only real systems man at a level that can ride control over Smith. Got it?

You'll be glad to hear, however, that the itch of your impatience will be scratched before it gets unbearable. I and Henry as well, have some ideas for an immediate operational foot-wetting, so prepare to put us down, back us up, what you will. But please don't start off again against the priority study. It won't save time, which is what you want, it will just waste more time, because it *has* to be done anyway. O.K.? We'll get going pronto.

Forward!

Frank

P.S. I apologize for including this P.S., Sam, since for you it would be routine anyway, but some of the others—Well, it's just a reminder, for those who need it, that all memos or anything in writing between us must be destroyed as soon as read. I'm afraid that will have to go for those marvelous backhand-Esperanto, or whatever they are, notes you make for yourself, too. Often wanted to ask—why do you do it? I've never known you to forget *anything*.

8

4 Oct
To: NOW
From: WFR
Re: Urgency

Dear Doc:

I never noticed till just now (NOW!) that your initials made an acronym. Prophetic? Let me repeat the assurance I made when you stopped by yesterday. No, we will not go off half-cocked. No. But we must get an actual job going, even if it turns up (or down) low on the priority list. If we don't, it will be months before we have a weighted-priority list that will suit you (or me, or any of us, for that matter) and we will become just another God-damned Committee to Study the Situation and Bring Back a Comprehensive Report. Fuck it. And let me assure you again that any project we undertake before we have our master plan weighed, polished, sharpened, and blessed at the font will be self-contained, limited, and "closed-ended," as Henry calls it.

We have a terribly big thing going, Noble, but we can't afford

143

to let it overwhelm us. If we contemplate it too long, or with *too* much respect, we will become paralyzed. Inevitably. Don't misunderstand. Nothing could be further from my mind, or from my guts, than minimizing in any way the awful responsibility we have taken on, or trivializing it, or relegating it to the category, however concealed, of another bureaucratic mission. But we still have to deal with it within the rubric of the feasible and face up to it. The only kind of mistake we can make at the beginning, Noble, will be to do something that isn't quite as urgent as it might be. As far as doing anything irrevocable that is just plain wrong—how could we? We'll be so damned cautious on this first trip that—well, you'll see.

One more thing. Procedure. We're going to use written memos, like this one, to avoid getting too bound in by the time-wasting inconveniences of waiting to see each other. But: Rule one—do your own typing or writing, no secretaries. Two—no copies or carbons. And three—destroy every memo you get as soon as you've read it. Immediately.

Avanti!

Frank

9

4 Oct
To: LP
From: WFR
Re: Normal birth pains
and their treatment

Dear Lew:

First a reminder—in temporary writing (writ on water, written in the sand?)—of what I told you in the office yesterday. All memos to be destroyed at once on reading, and, obviously—I guess I should have spelled this out to everybody also—no copies or other participants.

I think I'm going to need your help, personally, right away. The normal problems of getting a rather unstructured enterprise in operation are bound to be magnified in such a far-reaching responsibility as ours, or I should think they would, anyway, and we have one coming up forthwith. Noble Wilson's feet are getting a bit cold, and he's expressing it by insisting, or trying to insist, on holding off any operations until we have our priority list down cold. Which means, obviously, temporize while I work out my inner mental conflicts, etc., etc. No, I'm sure it's only temporary, so I'm not worried, but I'd appreciate your giving him some of your best Grade A psyching.

What will make it easier for us, I think, is that Sam Gold is unreasonably impatient to start on *any* operation, without any "meaningless moralizing," as he calls anything that isn't direct action. What *his* psyche needs I'll leave to you, but we have the makings of a trade-off here, or don't you recognize trade-offs in the psycho-education business? (If I were writing this to Sam I would refer, I hope winningly, to zero-sum games.) Anyway, I don't have to tell you that we *must* get a serious job done on priorities, but we must also get an operation in the works without delay, or we'll die.

This is going to come up at the next meeting—I'm still having to be coy on exact date, etc.—so I'd appreciate your help in particular. It should go without saying, but I'll be prudent and say it, that I also assume you will have your own ideas about the kind of first operation we should undertake and will not be shy about expressing them, no matter whose hands they play into. Let the chips fall, etc.

Best
Frank

10

Dear Arthur:

Reminder—as soon as you get that feasibility report in on the tax collection caper, call me. I have to set a date for the next session as quickly as I can, and the session itself has to be soon.

As you foresaw, we're going to get a good dialectic going between the action-now people and the let's-look-it-overs. Always works this way, doesn't it? I think I've done a fair job of giving all our respected members the necessary feeling of indispensability. One way or another.

President is pleased at the idea of opening with the tax caper. He says there are maybe a dozen in Congress he can talk openly with about our little game—he won't say whom, but they are mostly tax-minded and will like the notion of our collecting our own "appropriations" before we get on to the bigger things.

Your action group will be called, for budget purposes, Selective Services (for the Implementation of National Priority Programs). You'll get letterheads, listings, and so on; how you handle your dealings will be up to your usual discretion, and I don't want to know more than I have to. Pardon the repetition. Another thing I'll want for the meeting, even though I don't expect to use any of it till the next one, but just in case, is your tentative working list of major proposed projects, basic rationales, etc. Whatever you have. I want to be even more dazzling with my off-the-cuff for-instances than I am when I wear them *au naturel,* if you'd believe it.

I must hand it to you. I'm at the point of becoming as optimistic about this business as you said I'd be.

Burn it, baby, burn it
Frank

• Six months ago it was not unreasonable to suspect that Rooney might have been overextending himself. Evidently a subclimate of public feeling has developed meanwhile that has made this Commission and its objectives thinkable, if not yet speakable. Change, the rate of change, the accelerating rate of change, etc.—the clichés of uncomprehended social movement.

Rooney has not only been exquisitely sensitive to this feeling, unlike most men in high public office, but he has understood that the time was ripe once more for the people's leaders to follow their constituents' unexpressed inclinations. (The essence of leadership?) And he has been bold enough to move confidently in support of his understanding, and shrewd enough and experienced enough to move on it successfully, at least to the present point of setting up his "priorities" commission, his "selective services," and so on, and having them staffed exactly as he wants.

It is easy to say this, but consider what a formidable political achievement it must have been for Rooney to have brought it off. It commands respect, whatever else you may think of it. And yet, even as one says it, one realizes that if it had not been Rooney and his political maneuverings it would have been someone else in some other way; we are dealing with a political (sociological? ecological?) idea whose time has come, whoever the carrier.

The personnel of Rooney's little commission are more impressive than his manipulative messages to them would suggest, and they were most carefully chosen. The difficulties Rooney appears to be having (i.e., cautious Wilson vs. impatient Gold; suspicious Will McGee; timid bureaucrat Henry Harrison, etc.) are not the unexpected results of ill-thought choices. They are part of the ambience he has deliberately created for his assistant demigods; it is an ambience that ensures the kind of continuous dialectic Rooney thinks is essential to the success of the project. On the basis of how far he's gone already one must assume he's right unless and until he's proved wrong.

147

CHAPTER ELEVEN

1

—What I like best about my own proposal, I suppose, is that it sets us off on a self-sufficient basis. Economically, at least. There's a certain neatness to the idea of financing one's own activities that appeals to me. I don't know whether this comes from having been around budget-making agencies for so many years, or maybe from a traditional Puritan training as a boy—if you want a bicycle, Frank, you have to earn the money for it first. The second thing I like, I mean what I think of as the second most important advantage of this project at this time, is that it will be a comparatively quiet operation. There will be no catastrophe headlines, no inconvenient investigations that can take a lot of valuable time, and so on. So what if somebody notices that over a period of eight months the country loses a hundred and ten retired multimillionaires, instead of the thirty-odd actuarially expectable? Interesting, perhaps, but not suspicious, because there will be the full spectrum of causes, places, and circumstances. Number three. Although we ourselves will not know specifically who, when, and how, we will know in the aggregate what the financial results will be and what most of the direct public benefits, over and beyond expediting inheritance tax receipts, will be. Quite exactly, as a matter of fact. Fourth, and finally, I like the finite quality of the operation, the fact that it will be one of the comparatively few "retail" operations we will have had initiated. I think this will be good for our immortal souls in case any of us let ourselves rationalize away what we're doing in terms of abstract humanity. There will be individual people disposed of, some of whose names will be known to some of us to some degree, though none will be in any sense a friend or acquaintance. Since most of what we'll be doing later will become increasingly abstracted, I feel that starting with a project that requires the singling out of a list of specific individuals may help us maintain a sense of realism that some of us may not otherwise achieve.

—Frank, I'm not so sure I like this not knowing who's on the list. It seems irresponsible. Naturally, I'd be more *comfortable* not knowing, but this contradicts the last reason you gave for liking the project. And I definitely don't like the idea of an open John Doe death warrant, even when I'm the one who's signing it.

—Well, you're right, Will, when you catch my contradiction on the last reason, but not entirely. You won't be able to read the obit pages for the next eight months without wondering which ones you helped write, and you'll be bound to feel responsible for all those who meet the criteria for this operation even when you know that a third are leaving our world on their own private schedules with no assistance from us. And the criteria, incidentally, that I'm about to propose, and on which all Smith's figures are based, are explicit as hell. It's an open warrant, but not in the sense that Selective Services will have more than borderline options on whose name goes on the list. O.K.?

—Before you get around to the criteria for this particular operation, Frank, don't you think we should have clarified our general criteria for everything we do? It seems to me that we're going at this business of criteria ass-backwards. I don't see the need for going off half-cocked just to satisfy some emotional need to prove how activist we are. And with all due respect for the convenience of knocking off useless moneyholders, this is really not the purpose of our existence. We're not—or we shouldn't be, or think of our-

149

selves as—some damned band of superduper institutional Robin Hoods, I would think.

—*I* couldn't disagree with you more, Doc. I think that's just what we are, although I agree we can do without the romantic self-righteousness you imply. Our *basic* criterion—and we don't need to wait for a six-month study in depth to find out—is the general welfare, and if getting our own activities financed can't be assumed to be in that modest category, we shouldn't be here at all, talking about anything.

—Easy, Sam. Noble isn't implying self-righteousness, just urging caution. I don't agree with him on this one, but I think the principle is important that we never lose sight of what we're doing in the longer perspective. And I shouldn't have to say this, Sam, but if we don't accept each other's good faith on motive we're in trouble. Anyway, let's have these criteria you have in mind, Frank, if you can give them to us without a chalk talk.

—Glad you asked, Lew. Actually, they're rather simple, so some of you may be disappointed. So here we go. There are six of them, and all six must be met without any element of doubt. I have to emphasize this, because although we will later be engaged in generic operations, in which no attention will be paid to individual "participants"—that's my personal euphemism—this particular operation will be painstakingly selective, and it would be quite irresponsible not to treat it accordingly. Repeat: *All* criteria must be met, with no ambiguities, or name goes off list.

Very well. One: The net value to the public weal, in inheritance taxes and other useful distributions of the estate, must be not less than ten million dollars. That's arbitrary, of course, but measurable. You understand that we have access to all the information that would give us an accurate figure—assets, trust arrangements, testamentary provisions, expectable legal contests, and so on. Two: The participant must be someone engaged in no socially significant activities whatsoever. No political judgment involved here, tempting as it would be to exercise it—just a judgment of whether the participant is doing *anything* that might have a bearing on more than his own immediate private interests. Don't jump down my throat, Noble, about subjectivity—no one will be touched if there's the slightest chance he may be doing "something"—anything. We're after those who have in effect withdrawn from society and are waiting to die, gracefully or otherwise. Most of them, as it happens, will be very old women, but only because there are so many more of them. Actually, Smith's figures indicate that in the eighty-and-up group a higher proportion of women who have this kind of money are still active than men. Just thought you'd find it interesting. Three: A corollary of the last. There must be no prospect of the participant once more becoming engaged in such activities. By prospect I mean simple physical possibility, based on current medical knowledge—the state of the art, such as it is. It's simple logic—if we consider the second criterion valid we should not foreclose on the rights of these people to renew their memberships in society.

The fourth item is trickier. It concerns the weight we should give to the actuarial chances of our potential customers dying anyway. Our Selective Services, incidentally, are in a position to give excellent medical prognoses, in statistical terms. The two governing considerations I propose may seem contradictory. On the one hand it seems pointless to expedite the demise of those most likely to leave this world anyway during this period, since our interference with the course of their lives would have insufficient purpose. On the other hand, we are starting with a new program, and I don't think we'd be fudging if we leave alone those most likely to live on a good bit longer. So the proposal is to exempt those our experts believe have less than a 20 per cent or more than an 80 per cent chance of expiring naturally during the selection period. Arbitrary, but subject to revision. Think about it a little before you knock it. . . . Number five: There must be no plausible offsetting factors to the social benefit of the death of any of the participants. This involves a more subjective evaluation than I like, but since it is only an outside precaution I don't think it's unreasonable. An example might be a case in which the death of the controlling owner of a large enterprise might lead to negative, or at least unknown, social consequences.

And finally, for reasons which may seem politically unprincipled but which I think are psychologically sound, we would strike from the list anyone otherwise qualified who is known to any of us personally. This is not to protect friends—it's not an insiders' ploy —but to eliminate any kind of emotional interest. Smith's group should know if any candidate is known to any of us, but nevertheless I ask you—assuming this project is approved—to turn in the names of anyone you know who you think may have won a place on our list.

—Very interesting, Frank, but before we go into the pros and cons I'm curious about the figures you threw out earlier. You referred to a hundred and ten victims—participants—of which about a third would die anyway, if I heard you correctly. What are these figures based on, or did you mean them only to be exemplary?

—They're real figures, Bill, but only estimates. I had Smith work them out from data he has already, but we don't think they'll be too far off what they come up with when we go ahead.

—How does that one-third figure jibe with the 20-to-80- per cent range you're proposing? Don't you have a normal distribution?

—No, Bill; that's the way the curve skews.

—How is it that Smith would have such data on hand? Seems very curious to me.

—It is indeed curious, Noble. That's one of the reasons Smith is uniquely qualified to work with us. He has done this kind of work before, privately, experimentally, and, I must say, completely ethically. As I told you, I have total confidence in him and his special group, but I'd rather not go into more detail, on the same principle by which we should not, and will not, know the details of operations we authorize now and later. Since I knew this question would come up, I arranged for him *not* to be here this time, although he's near enough if we need him. I'll answer questions about him, but only up to a point, and I'd be grateful for as few as possible, preferably none.

—You're turning it into a vote of confidence in yourself, you sly son of a bitch! O.K., I'll buy it. No questions. . . . Yes, one. Will you tell us some of the things he's done?

—Thank you again, Will. Without naming names, I'll just say that he and his associates are responsible for expediting some rather important civic improvements. From upgrading art museums, colleges, and hospitals to making good housing possible, for the resuscitation of moribund industries, for raising the standards of highway drivers, and for an enormous variety of public welfare work over the last several years. He has been part of a group, which is now in effect our Selective Services division, which has been able to effectuate the longer view of the general welfare on a limited and private basis well before we could take our recognitions of necessity to the operational level exhibited here. Excuse the jargon, please, but I have to protect myself, don't I? And to answer Noble's question, he and his associates have had to develop an invaluable data bank in most unusual, but relevant for us, areas. As for integrity and moral commitment, I will say simply that I'll put my own name on the line for it without qualification. Any more questions? This is not a request. . . . Thank you.

—Frank, you've gone into quite a bit of detail for your proposed opener. I'm at a disadvantage without any surveys, cost figures, or even place names, but I would like the group to consider the possible plusses of a single purgative event, like the burning down of a slum, over the project you propose. I'm not getting into a contest with you, Frank, and I'm in favor of getting going on any rational enterprise, but I'd like to know the thinking of the group in general.

—Certainly, Henry! Gentlemen, the option posed by Mr. Harrison is this: Might it not be better for us to plan a one-shot, catastrophic, cleaning type of operation rather than the detailed, selective one I suggested for our first project? I'd like to hear first from whoever thinks it would be. I don't, but I won't feel rebuffed if you vote me down. We do want something limited, encompassable, and easy to put into prompt operation. Bill?

—Would Henry be more specific? If he doesn't have a particular project in mind, would he give us an example of the kind of "purgative" he means? How big, how elaborate, with what immediate objective?

—I had in mind something like a slum clearance, Bill. I keep thinking of that Chicago catastrophe last spring. You *saw* what came out of it—how marvelously Frank turned a disaster into one of the biggest advances in public housing and education we've ever seen. I don't think any of us would argue that this wasn't an appropriate prototype for us. That was an accident, of course, but it could well be planned again. I'm sure there are areas where the cost-benefit ratio would be even more favorable, and I should think our Services team could come up with a good selection quite quickly. Another kind of single project would be the elimination, by disaster, of a single large complex devoted to the maintenance of the unproductive, like a large welfare establishment, insane asylum, or such.

—I see Dr. Wilson is ready to comment.

—Damned right, Frank. This is exactly what I meant when I talked about the danger of going off half-cocked. First of all, the proposition is much too general at this stage of our collective life as a commission. But more important, any of the examples Henry mentioned would in effect commit us to programs that may very well be entirely contradictory to the orientation of our priorities as we determine them later. This is not temporizing, I assure you, but a real problem. Supposing, for example, we decide that our program for housing—if indeed we decide to have one at all, which is by no means certain—should be directed not toward the elimination, or improvement, of slums but toward *aggravating* slum conditions, to expedite a more revolutionary plan. Or perhaps our program will require the elimination of slums without rebuilding. We don't know. And the same goes for asylums and the like—we don't yet know what our long-range program will be. Which means that the possibility exists—a real one—that we may be committing not a mass reduction of problems, as Frank puts it, but wanton killing. No, I can't buy it, unless somebody can prove to me that the specific project—not just the general type, Henry—will fit whatever priority system we devise, and I don't see how that can be guaranteed at this stage of the game. I don't want to keep harping on it, but for all our coolness, our responsibility is quite unprecedented. I'm prepared to make mistakes, and big ones, and stomach them, but we have no excuse for making mistakes from carelessness or inconsistency. Now, I won't pretend that I'm crazy about Frank's elegant little caper. I think I've made it clear that I see no compelling reason for doing anything in a hurry. But at least *it* has the advantage of being sufficiently outside the mainstream of any long-range program so that it can be judged more or less independently of general priorities. It is a money-raising, or supportive, project, not a substantive one, so I suppose it can be evaluated in those terms. But I'm still for holding off.

—Well, thank you, Noble, for your enthusiastic support. . . . Sam?

—Exception. I take exception to everything Doc said. It sounds logical, except for one small point—it just ain't so. Any of the projects Henry mentioned, as well as Frank's thing, are perfectly legitimate whatever priority level they fall at. . . . Because these are the kinds of people and the kinds of situations we're here to eliminate, period. If it comes out that some slum-clearance blast we put through doesn't fit exactly on the schematic chart we draw up six months from now, what the hell? We have still got rid of a lot of those we know it's our job to get rid of, and we know have to be got rid of—so what if they don't fit into our neat construct that we will have worked out later? That construct could be just as wrong as any decision we make today, but the principle will be the same.

155

If Noble thinks that one kind of killing under the same principle is somehow more or less morally defensible than another, I'd like him to explain how. He made a casual jump in which he equated the moral propriety of the terms of our commission with consistency to a systems construct we haven't even worked out yet. It's ironic. *I'm* the systems man here, and I'm accustomed to being the one charged with this logical gambit myself.

—Lewis Perkins, did I detect an expression of desire to have the floor, or was it only wishful thinking?

—Yes, Frank, if you mean will I be your shill. A motion. In the interest of keeping ourselves from being divided by the bigger purposive questions at this point in our collective life as a commission, and in the interest of getting ourselves going, and in the interest of not getting bogged down, and in the interest of exercising and testing our new equipment—the Selective Services—and in the interest of covering ourselves on finances if we run into budget problems *sub rosa,* and in the interest of maintaining the mental health and welfare of Frank Rooney, I move we proceed with his tax-expediting project as outlined. But unanimously, please!

—You've heard the question, put to you somewhat irregularly. Is it your purpose to approve the proposal? Never mind his damfool reasons, please! Henry? Will McGee? Bill Spaatz? Sam? Noble? Very good. Done!

2

8 Oct
To: AS
From: WFR
Re: Tax collection

Dear Arthur:

As expected, we can go ahead on this project as planned. Refine your figures, be conservative as hell, take no chances about any wrongos being entered on the list. Provide a chronology, with a rationale, the same kind you gave me. Furnish vital statistics, furnish financial data with breakdowns, everything that will remind our people how thorough, accurate, and reliable you are. Which of course you are, but the name of *your* game at the moment is Getting To Know You. I am very optimistic.

The meeting went about as we expected. The level of discussion was distressingly low. If we didn't know enough not to take it at face value, we should want to liquidate the commission before it does *anything*, in our own self-defense. The nit-picking was not exactly Aesopian, but it had an obvious overlay of Freudian thobbery. I think everyone knew, consciously or damned near it, that the so-called debate was an acting out of misgivings, fear, guilt, and —excuse the expression—insecurity.

Once we are under way—and I expect you to let them *all* know simultaneously that dispositions of participants are being made, have been made, how many, etc.—all these "principled" differences will fade. I cannot think of any stronger bond between men, anything more certain to dissolve pseudo-ideological and pseudo-philosophical and pseudo-moral conflicts, than deep complicity in a great violation of the social contract. The greater the distance between the actions committed by the conspirators and an understanding of them by the spokesmen for conventional morality, the greater the bond. Whatever neat phrase you or I may choose to attach to the nature of their activities—our activities—it is still a guilty conspiracy, emotionally, and this is what will hold us together and enable us to function. This, of course, is the real reason I was so insistent on a quick project, and this one in particular, with its emphasis in person-by-person selection, which we're not likely to see again. I leveled with them—up to a point! They took it. They're a good group, and I don't think I made any mistakes in picking them.

How's your proposed project list coming along—the *real* priorities study? Keep swinging, baby!

As ever

Frank

3

Washington, Oct. 8—The President's Special Commission on
National Priorities will propose specific timetables for urgent
and important national programs, it was announced here
today. According to Dr. William Francis Rooney, chairman
of the group, the recent charge made by Rep. Otha Greer (R.,
O.) that the new committee was established to pacify public
demand for action by furnishing "pretentiously regurgitated
banalities" was an "understandable slander."

Dr. Rooney, whose name is normally associated here with
colorful invective, was uncharacteristically calm at hearing
Rep. Greer's charge. "Fundamentally, you know, he's right
about committees like ours, and I don't blame him at all for
his skepticism," he said. "It's a slander, of course, but an
understandable one. I think if I were in his shoes I'd have the
same feeling.

"However, the facts are a little different—as when are they
not? We plan to run a committee of a different color, you
might say. So much data is already available to assist in the
implementation of existing priority programs that much of
what we'll do will consist of quiet, and if necessary not so
quiet, prodding of appropriate agencies to get things going
that they already have the mandate, the appropriations, and
the other logistical necessities to put into effect. I don't think
many people realize how much, or how many, of the big, and
sometimes revolutionary, changes in social programs can be
handled without further legislation.

"It is our plan to operate in a manner exactly contrary to
that normally associated with committees charged with grandiose functions. We will not, as Mr. Greer so reasonably
expects, go under water for a year and a half and return to
the surface bearing a treasure of golden declarations and
ringing pronouncements. We will work, we hope, with minimum publicity. While we are working out our masterpiece of
priority program planning for Mr. Greer and his friends on
the Appropriations Committee to eviscerate later, we expect

158

to accomplish enough by way of effectively irritating executive agencies and legislative bodies in the interim to be able to tell Appropriations not only what we think they should do but what we ourselves have already done.

"As I said, we are not only not seeking publicity, we are trying to avoid it. But for the sake of example only, I will let Mr. Greer know that we are already engaged in a program to increase the efficiency of revenue collections of various sorts to such an extent that I think the figures that Mr. Greer's committee will look at a year or so from now will surely earn us his approval. And perhaps even an apology or two, although we can live happily without one."

Dr. Rooney requested that his remarks about the setting of specific timetables not be quoted directly. He acknowledged that his commission had had its second formal meeting today, but indicated that there would be no further announcements forthcoming of commission meetings and activities.

Rep. Greer was not available for further comment on Dr. Rooney's remarks.

4

New York, Oct. 18—Alexander Houten, patriarch of one of America's richest families, died here in his sleep yesterday at the age of 84.

Mr. Houten, who had been out of the public eye for many years after resigning his many financial, philanthropic, and public posts simultaneously in 1967, had retired to a near-recluse existence in his town house here, according to those who remained in touch with him in recent years. He left no immediate survivors.

Mr. Houten's death marks the final dispersion of the once-concentrated wealth of one of the last of the great nineteenth-century fortunes still remaining in the hands of a single survivor. Although Mr. Houten shared the inheritance of his father, Peter Houten, with two brothers and two sisters, all now deceased, he was the only heir of the noted steel tycoon to advance and multiply the family fortunes on his own during the 1920s, '30s, and '40s. His only son, Peter Houten II, died by his own hand in 1940.

Services will be held Friday morning at the Riverview Church, the construction of which had been inspired and financed by Mr. Houten's father. The President, the Governor, and civic leaders from all walks of life have indicated they will attend.

(For a full story of Mr. Houten's life and activities, see page 22.)

• THEY'RE OFF and running. From what we know of Smith and company's previous track record, it is certain that Project Number One will be executed carefully, effectively, responsibly, and, above all, cleanly. So much for that. But it does seem a rather trivial enterprise, in terms of what the grand high executioners were constituted to achieve. Noble Wilson could have carried off his objections to "institutional Robin Hoods" much more effectively, and possibly scuttled it with ridicule, were it not for his strong underlying commitment to the success of the Commission and for his understanding that sinking Rooney's first operation would mean sinking the entire program.

There is, indeed, a certain incongruity between the scope of this "assassination bureau" kind of caper and the long-range comprehensiveness of what these people intend to do. But the two may not be entirely incompatible. The given of the enterprise, the feeling that something truly drastic will be needed to reverse the entropic processes of contemporary society, dates back many years. Who knows how many secret Rooney-type plans were drawn up to deal

160

with them? Generalizations, crying of doomsday and the like—from scientists, social thinkers, literary types, preachers—may not have been limited to rhetoric.

Engaging in this kind of speculation is fruitless, if not necessarily paranoid, but it is relevant to the present project. The fact is that Rooney is getting his show on the road. However limited the scope, he is at long last operational—under official auspices. It is not to be denigrated.

CHAPTER TWELVE

1

22 Oct
To: All
From: WFR
Re: Priorities

SINCE our discussion yesterday was somewhat unfocused, I thought it might be helpful if I attempted to clarify our consensus on priorities for elimination by setting them down on paper. If I am wrong in what I think we agree on, or if I inadvertently (!) phrase my understanding of what we said with a slant in favor of my own line, I have absolute confidence that I will be put straight, by one or all of you. So here goes.

It was generally agreed, after long and random debate—discursion would be more like it, wouldn't you say?—that so far as we are concerned, *national* priorities, in the usual sense of making a shopping list of health, housing, cleaning the air, and so forth, with a value judgment attached (that such an item is number one on the list and such another is number five) would be of little real use to our mission, except to relieve the itch of our compulsions. We might agree, more or less, that trying to recapture a "viable" environment would be number one over the long pull, but what would that tell us that we don't already know about whom to

162

eliminate first or fifth? It is a premise of our assignment that the elimination of problems (in the form of people), selectively evaluated by *function,* is essential to holding the line against general breakdown and is a precondition to advancing the quality of life in any appreciable way. Therefore, only the priority of the eliminations themselves concerns us.

The point is that we don't need to know which big issues can be attacked first. But we can categorize the "participants" in our activities (I still like that word for them best) in terms of general hopelessness for earning their room and board in a contracting world. We will, as I suggested three weeks ago, be practicing triage, as the medical do, though in an obverse way: i.e., we will *hold off* our actions *against* those who may be redeemed by some new social development (medical discovery?) until we have disposed of those who are, by our standards, hopeless cases (in medical terms, the terminals). O.K. so far?

Group One, the top of our list, should include those who most actively drain off our resources, and who are therefore, by class, socially hopeless. Some examples. First, we agreed, come the medical "keep-alives" (including psychiatric, retarded, etc.), chiefly because they represent such a great per capita cost. Some exceptions, of course, but most are in hospitals or the equivalent, where terminal maintenance cases are always expensive. Next in this group, perhaps, are the unproductive aged, the hopelessly handicapped, and the incorrigibly indigent, a large proportion of whom are also in institutions. Here we also include fully committed addicts; it was suggested that our operations groups work out criteria to save, for the time being, the minority of addicts who are somewhat productive or who might profitably be rehabilitated. Recidivist criminals, in the old-fashioned sense, will go here too, but we heard a general insistence that the criteria of definition be especially rigorous with this group. Perhaps too many of us (all of us?) find it too easy to identify with criminals, unless we define them in such a way that nobody can mistake *us* for *them.* (Am I being unfair? All right, I

163

am being unfair.) And we also discussed a special sub-class here, the social terrorists, the would-be destroyers of anything in the *status quo,* regardless of proximate or long-term effects. They require, we agreed, two kinds of special care in definition: first, to limit ourselves to the true destroyers; and second, to make sure that persons under consideration may not be in effect allies and helpers in our own program. (I think we'll find quite a few like that.) Even when they're killing the wrong people they may well help establish the ambience we'll need for a background to our own operations fairly soon. All this, of course, we'll go into with Smith's group when we have our session on Ways and Means.

After we are well under way in the elimination of Group One, we should begin operations on Group Two, as I understood the sense of our discussion. It was not, we agreed, a matter of proceeding *seriatim,* one major group after another, but of overlapping sufficiently to conceal, or at least camouflage, the hard defining lines of the preceding group. Another reason noted was that Group Two—this is true of all groups except Group One—is so extensive that planning operations for it will require longer lead time than any of the categories in Group One. Very well. Our second group consists of the unemployable and unproductive. This means, for example, a high percentage of those on welfare or requiring similar assistance from relief programs. In general, this very large and amorphous group, though clearly dissipating our resources rather than contributing to them, does not effect a per capita cost comparable to Group One. It would be appropriate to note here—though I admit we didn't discuss it—that we should plan only on a partial program in Group Two. Whereas I would expect that we will clean out something like 75 per cent of those defined in Group One, perhaps even more, the figure in Group Two will probably be closer to 30 per cent. And, of course, a larger proportion of those who participate in Group Two will be wasted, in the sense that they would have been spared if the means available permitted individual distinctions in the large-scale operations we will necessarily use.

164

Whereas with the first group both the number and quality of the "wasted" participants will be such that none of us will lose any sleep over them, it will be well that by the time we begin operations on Group Two we are rid of any remnants of personal involvement. This means any kind of close examination of the groups of participants. It means leaving more and more of the selection to our Selective Services after we give them the guidelines. By the time we get to Two, not to mention Three, Four, and Five, we will have had to arrive at the emotional plateau that our older members did in World War II—where we know we are fighting for a just and necessary cause and where we accept the proposition that to prevail we will have to destroy millions of innocents along with our true enemies. We are all familiar with this emotional necessity, and what we have here is an absolute analogue. The only difference is that now we are making the decisions rather than carrying them out. Please excuse the interpolation; I simply felt that this was the place for it. For in Group Two we will be doing things as big and as undiscriminating as anything in warfare. We will not have established institutions at hand to define our categories for us. No buffer. We will be wiping out large areas, and we must recognize, accept, and then put away our consciousness of, the price. O.K.?

Comes now Group Three, and although it will be even harder to define precisely than Group Two, it will have to be started fairly soon, since the means required for disposing of these people will necessarily be pervasive and gradual rather than cataclysmic. These are our social incompetents. We will eliminate a fair share of them, because they offer us a more or less eugenic basis of selection, when we reach the stage where we face up to the fact that we will be operating to meet a *de facto* quota. Some of the means are already in effect, thanks to the advance cooperation of certain industries and regulatory agencies. We are talking of those people who make life more dangerous, more expensive, more physically wearing and psychologically frustrating, more generally destructive, for the rest of us. They might be defined, oddly enough, by

165

the means that we choose to eliminate them. For instance, you are all familiar with the recent improvements announced for the American automobile; you *may* also know that these improvements will not only introduce a new hazard to automobile driving but also that it will tend to eliminate only dangerous and irresponsible drivers; you do *not* know that certain people in the industry whose understanding of long-range problems resembles our own planned it that way. You have heard something about a new drug that is claimed to offer all the mood-changing benefits that a wrought-up nation could want; you have heard me say that it is being tested for approval for over-the-counter sale and that it will eventually be O.K.'d; you have *not* heard me say, before now, that it will be a real killer for intelligences and personalities weak enough to become dependent on it—and that this is no accident either. There's a spectacular new food additive in the works—I'll hold off on that till we get to Group Four. Of course, many other industries have been working in our vineyard all along, but usually through greed and unconcern, not programmatically.

As you see, I've been interpolating information again that I could have provided during our meeting. I held out till now because I thought I would put it to you in the context where it would mean the most. We will surely have to develop an imaginative selection of means to cope with the variety of species of participant-candidates that fall under this rubric. In general, in Group Three the rule will be: Let the punishment fit the crime. The punishment will seem harsh indeed by conventional standards (that is, in terms of the individual crime) but it will be appropriate and necessary for the rest of us to survive. End of pious moral stricture.

Group Four is trickier. It belongs somewhere between One and Two (by the standards of per capita drain on our resources) but we have to set it back in the priority table because we have less control over it. These are the people in the most backward countries, those who are not only not self-supporting but who never will be, and who will never be thinned out enough to support themselves except by uncontrolled natural catastrophe, famine, war, or other population control mechanism. Or by us. At some point we will have to act on a large scale in these countries, when we get clearance. The food additive I started to mention before, which is already in use in some of these areas, will have a number of interesting side effects (selectively fatal) that we will probably want to develop further.

Group Four will involve a more traditional form of genocide, except that we will not be inspired by the traditional motives— political and mercenary. Although there are endless precedents, the most explicitly relevant is that of the Peruvian Amazon Company at the turn of the century; they simply executed inefficient workers. Another, in our own time, has been the extermination of Brazilian Indians by land-grabbers. I am deliberately citing conventionally horrendous examples to underscore the point again that *purpose* is the criterion every time. What was done in the Amazon was motivated by private profit, free enterprise following its own logic unrestrained. Some means are aesthetically more acceptable than others, but it is the ends sought and *achieved* that matter. *Our* object is the survival of the most survivable. End of second pious stricture.

We didn't discuss Group Five. This is the far more drastic matter of general population reduction, period. If we cannot get far enough in our selective weeding, we may have to revert to the established methods of natural selection, intensified. No criteria, except better they than us, and variants thereof. Nothing to plan for at this point—but something to keep in mind in case we start to worry about not being fussy enough with our methods of selection in Groups One through Four. Being *too* careful may turn out to be self-defeating waste.

That's the consensus, or at least my version of it, with a few side dishes. Whoever thinks I have not properly expressed our collective views, or who wants further clarification on any of the new points I threw in—get back to me soonest.

Frank

22 Oct
To: WFR
From: HSH
Re: Priorities

Dear Frank:

I hope you don't find my questions nit-picking, but I don't like to be uncertain.

First, in Group One. By keep-alives we're clear, from all our talk about them, what *we* mean. But do I understand you make no distinction between the terminals as defined by the institutions maintaining them and the keep-alives as *we* define them? I would guess that the distinction would be tactical in each particular case, and that we will use our own definition except where it would make the operation too difficult. Correct?

Second, I don't see why or how our "emotional" problem, if any, will be that much different between Groups Two-Three-Four-Five and Group One. It seems to me that we've all burned our bridges on our commitment to this project some time ago. Or is this section—I suddenly realize, knowing you—actually addressed to one particular member you think may need this kind of bucking up?

Three. When you say—and this did not come out of our meeting as part of any consensus unless I was asleep, hardly likely—that the social incompetents might be defined by the means we choose to eliminate them, aren't you being a little glib? It seems to me that a listing and a more comprehensive kind of definition is in order here. Do you have the makings of such a list, or is one being worked up by S.S.? Our discussion was clear, but we never did get down to definitions.

Four. It seems important to me that we know all the details of the private programs you refer to—the automobiles, the drug, the food preservative. As well as any others you *didn't* mention. Will we get them? Soon?

Five. I guess there were only four.

As ever

Henry

(THIS memo was returned to sender with the following appended in longhand: To *all* your questions, expressed and implied: yes, of course. *WFR*)

3

23 Oct
To: WFR
From: NOW
Re: So-called priorities

Dear Frank:

No questions. No clarifications wanted at this time. No objections to your constructive additions to our discussion. No general objection to your interpretations.

Just my usual cautionary. It is so predictable by now that I hope you really read it. I sometimes wonder. It is this: that however casual we may be in *discussing* bases of selection, it will be a fundamental ground rule that no program actually be instituted until—

1. We shall have arrived at precise and unambiguous *definitions* of the category of participants to be liquidated in that particular operation.

2. With all due respect to the Selective Services division, all *data* submitted by them about any group or sub-group shall have been independently examined, questioned, analyzed, and confirmed by us before we proceed to use it as a basis for authorizing operations.

169

3. Although Selective Services will operate independently from us in respect to time and place of operations, all *means* to be used by them in executing assignments shall have been approved by us in advance for the group in question.

Please confirm

Noble

(MEMO returned to sender with following longhand notation: ABSOLUTELY! *Frank*)

4

23 Oct
To: WFR
From: RWMcG
Re: Means and ends

Dear Frank:

I wouldn't have phrased our general meeting of minds quite as you did, but I won't object to it as a working understanding. Your additions were helpful. However, I am concerned about one area of your memo.

It is the general question of means. I am aware that we will have exhaustive discussion on means, and of course we will have to consider and approve whatever means are proposed by Selective Services. And I am sure you have no intention to short-circuit our consideration of their proposals. But the tone of your memo disturbs me. It implies, I feel, that *you* feel that the means we use to eliminate the groups in question are entirely tactical, that you pretend not to realize to what extent the means we choose will either confirm the rightness of our ends or corrupt them.

I know, of course, that you *do* have an exquisite sense of the relationship between means and ends, and I don't wish to suggest that I am more-sensitive-than-thou. But when you toss out a piece of palpable nonsense, when you say of the Group Three participants that they "might be defined by the means that we choose to eliminate them," I wonder if you are deliberately trying to foster a kind of slap-happiness among us—presumably to ease our inevitable tenseness and guilt about what we're doing. You seem to be saying that since what we're doing is right, let's not get exercised over such petty details as how we accomplish it.

I am over-simplifying, and I may be unfair, but I do detect this tone and I think it's a dangerous one. I'm all for maintaining our sense of motion, our perspective, a light touch in our communications, and for avoiding that over-solemnity that can asphyxiate, but the operating decisions we make are life-and-death matters on the largest scale. As a matter of *fact*. If we get to the point where we have to keep kidding ourselves, in behalf of maintaining our sanity, that these decisions are part of a game or that they should *not* weigh heavily upon us, we're in the wrong business and we should get out and turn it over to somebody else.

> *As ever, Frank, nothing personal,*
> *Will*

(MEMO returned to sender with following longhand notation: Your point well taken, but I must defend the phrase that I used that you quoted as evidence. It was another way of saying that since Group Three participants will have to be defined functionally, rather than by their condition, means and definitions will have to be established at the same time. And I plead not guilty to your charges of trying to dilute the seriousness of our decision-making. You know me well enough to know that my "slap-happiness" is style and nothing more. At the moment I can't think of a single operational detail we'll have to consider that I'd call petty. O.K.? *Frank)*

(MEMO sent again to original recipient with following longhand notation: Of course, Frank. But I wanted you to say so, explicitly. And thanks for doing it so graciously. *Will)*

5

> 23 Oct
> To: WFR
> From: AS
> Re: Group One operations-means

Dear Frank:

Here is the preliminary report from Selective Services on means suggested for Group One. I have schematized it as a chart for quick reference. Explanatory notes follow:

MEANS, GROUP ONE:

Preliminary proposals for dealing with participants so classified. Listed by sub-group and indicated preferential order of application.

1. Institutional keep-alives, terminal and near terminal.
   (a) Drugging. (b) Incidental epidemics. (c) Physical catastrophe.
2. Non-institutionalized keep-alives.
   (a) Drugging. (b) Critical withdrawal of services.
3. Noncontributory institutionalized aged, handicapped, and incorrigibly indigent.
   (a) Incidental epidemics. (b) Physical catastrophe. (c) Drugging. (d) Diversion of public protection personnel.
4. The same, non-institutionalized.
   (a) Double-drugging. (b) Area epidemics. (c) Area catastrophe. (d) Critical withdrawal of services.

172

5. Drug addicts.
   (a) Overdosing. (b) Escalation. (c) Contamination. (d) *Ad hoc* procedures.
6. Criminals.
   (a) Penal escalation. (b) Death squads. (c) Provocation.
7. Social terrorists.
   (a) Addiction. (b) Provocation.

1. For institutionalized keep-alives, terminal and near terminal. The method of choice here is (a), simple over-drugging, under-drugging, or incorrect drugging, wherever attending medical personnel will cooperate. We have reason to know this will be possible in far more cases than you might expect, probably in a majority of terminal institutions. In general, the medical profession has been far ahead of the rest of us, both in discussion and in increasingly frequent independent action. Our experience indicates that with a minimum of disinterested outside encouragement, this will be the most effective, economical, and natural procedure for this subgroup. Where general medical cooperation is not available, but where other inside assistance can be arranged, we recommend the use of (b), "incidental epidemics." E.g., serum hepatitis, bacterial food poisoning, admixture of common high-reaction drugs in foods, application of bacteria and viruses to bedding, etc. Where no medical cooperation is available, or where complex bureaucratic processes may interfere, we recommend (c), physical catastrophes—fires, explosions, heat and power breakdowns in cold weather, basic water supply contamination, etc. In general, this means must be adopted with moderation and under stringent limitations.

2. For non-institutionalized keep-alives. These must be handled on an *ad hoc* basis by cooperating medical personnel, custodians, and others in a position to take action. The principal means will remain (a), drugging, as above; (1b) and (1c) will normally be

173

inapplicable. Another useful procedure here will be (b), critical withdrawal of services: unavailability of nurse, doctor, or custodian at essential times; leaving participant unattended; non-delivery of essential medicines. Since this category will account for only a small part of Group One participants, the reason for giving it attention is that these actions will be helpful as background ambience for the more important programs. A relatively small number of such cases can give a surprisingly high proportion of the population some feeling of indirect involvement, which in turn will accelerate the acceptability of the bigger operations.

3. For the noncontributory institutionalized aged, handicapped, and incorrigibly indigent. Here we anticipate that (a), incidental epidemics, will be the most common type of operation, but with more variations than the examples cited in (1b). Physical catastrophe, (b), will be the second means of choice. (Despite its convenience, (c), drugging, will be less applicable here, since medical cooperation will be less available, and opportunities for mis-drugging more limited.) A variant we will develop for this sub-group will be (d), a system for diverting public protection personnel—firemen, policemen, emergency squads, building inspectors, water controllers, etc.—from conventional responses to catastrophes and to normal functions. Part of this system will consist of misdirection, which in slum neighborhoods is already the case with respect to fire alarms, and part will consist of conventional subornation and corruption. We anticipate no important complications. With this procedure, the general breakdown of public services that contributes to the motivation of our overall program will fortuitously expedite its own correction.

4. For the same, non-institutionalized. Although we will have to deal with these to a certain extent *ad hoc,* there are too many in this sub-group to leave it entirely to individual initiatives. (a), what we call double-drugging, will require the enlistment of cadres of individual physicians, pharmacists, and clinic personnel. Put simply, it will call for the use of standards of prescription for this

174

category of participant different from those in general practice. We are preparing a model "black book" pharmacopeia that cooperating medical personnel can use as a guide. For pharmacists we have already prepared a compatible schedule of suggested drug switches they can safely use on clients they will help us terminate. (If commission members are surprised that so many of our proposed means require the cooperation of so many outside parties, they should know that we have already established, from our previous private work, a substantial network of associates in strategic occupations.) (b) and (c) are larger-scale equivalents of institutional epidemics and physical catastrophes. Their parameters of operation will be residential areas that our statistical research shows to contain a predetermined minimum percentage of qualifiers (the percentage of course to be set by the commission). These studies need not be wastefully precise, for the convenient reason that Group One non-qualifiers in such areas will usually qualify in other categories, especially Group Two. Finally, we expect to handle most of the individual cases that cannot be dealt with by (a), (b), or (c) by (d), critical withdrawal of services, but we do not, realistically, expect a high yield here.

5. Drug addicts. We have not yet completed our proposed criteria for distinguishing addicts with a reasonable chance of redemption (to positive productivity, not merely rehabilitation from addiction). We can say at this time that they will constitute a small minority. With this sub-group, (a), our basic procedure, is comparatively simple and foolproof, and has the considerable advantage of long informal use by interested medical, social service, and law enforcement personnel. It is overdosing, and it can be implemented on a large scale in a variety of ways. One simple system, used experimentally in New York last year, consists of introducing heroin of unusually high purity into regular distribution channels. The effect on users—double- or even triple-dosing—is fatal to those already on high intake levels or in poor general condition. (They tend, of course, to be the same persons, as well as to be the least

redeemable.) A variant we are optimistic about, which has also been tested experimentally, (b), calls for escalating the dependency of the unredeemably addictive personality. Many users of hallucinogens, alcohol, marijuana, amphetamines, barbiturates, tobacco, etc., who can be so described and who we know will become Group One or Two qualifiers sooner or later, can be brought up to their natural level of dependency (on heroin, cocaine, and the like) with a little encouragement; if it is high enough they can then be dealt with by overdosing or other means. (This was also tried in New York, early in 1970; the "panic" in marijuana, plus the availability of cheap heroin, "promoted" thousands of such persons.) Overdosing can also be achieved by creating an ambience of higher-than-necessary consumption, with the aid of other drugs that increase the apparent sense of demand, or by making available, as we will be, an over-the-counter heroin blend that addicts will find helpful but will not associate with their daily "fix" quota. (c) will involve processing needles and other addict equipment with virulent diseases and poisons, and distributing them in an attractive manner. (d), for the institutionalized addicts, will be a grab-bag of *ad hoc* procedures administered by cooperating personnel—double-drugging, deliberate custodial carelessness, psychological discouragement, etc. (Actually, most institutions for addicts tend to promote failure in any case, since their objective, like ours, is to get them off the books, one way or another.)

6. Criminals. We have nearly completed an enforceable working definition of the kind of confirmed criminal element that fits the sense of our Group One program. We will forward it shortly. I would be most surprised if any member takes issue with it or can find reason for concern that the wrong people—like ourselves, for instance, as you pointed out in your last memo—might fall into this category. Our principal procedure, (a), can be generally defined as the intensification of present penal systems. Since the purpose of prisons has always been, regardless of euphemisms about "correction" and "rehabilitation," the physical separation of inconvenient segments of society, the groundwork has been laid for us. Politi-

cally, we are not yet in a position to introduce the old English all-purpose death penalty, but we will have the enthusiastic cooperation of police and prison personnel in developing the practical proposition that every sentence for a felony is likely to be, *de facto,* capital. Sample techniques: provocation of jail riots, with retaliation by mass killing rather than selective sanctions; willful and conspicuous disregard for safety and sanitary practices, with more and bigger jail fires, explosions, asphyxiation, food poisoning, epidemics; individual killings between prisoners deliberately crowded and associated for that purpose. It will soon be made clear to qualifying prisoners that killing as many of them as can be rationalized will be the *intention* of the prison system; this will encourage jailbreaks and other acts of desperation, which in turn will rationalize further acceleration in killing off the prison population. However, in providing a sense of legitimacy to prison personnel for expediting the destruction of the imprisoned criminal class, the program may move too fast; we will have prepared a slowdown procedure to avoid the embarrassment of what could otherwise be a total prison cleanout in six months. Also, since once the program gets under way it will become almost impossible to differentiate between true criminals, by our standard, and others, it is essential that we get the non-criminals out of the institutions to be destroyed before the program commences. We will have such a scheme worked out for this purpose shortly, and we will forward it with our proposed working definition. It will need political implementation, but only on a manipulable administrative level.

Since (a) will achieve virtually 100 per cent success for the confined criminals, no other method is needed. For the majority of the criminal class, the unconfined, we propose two principal methods. (b), which as you know is already in effect in several large cities, although aimed at social dissidents rather than criminals, is the establishing of police "death squads," on the Brazilian model. Their existence must be flaunted openly, as in Brazil, clearly indicating centralized direction. But we must also establish fear of retaliation among the cooperating police for not following the rules

177

we set up for the selection of victims, or it will get out of hand. The only operating problem here is one of control. (c) involves provoking large-scale internal warfare among organized criminals. With the use of traditional methods—double informers, planted misinformation, general frame-ups, etc.—this will provide a substantial yield with minimum cost and risk.

7. Social terrorists. Here also we are working out a definition, in order to eliminate ambiguities and possible future misunderstandings. The distinction will not be moral or political, but practical, keyed only to the question: Is the kind of destruction practiced by the group under consideration consistent with, or counter-productive to, our own objectives? Your intuition that many of these people may be allies, in a practical sense, is perceptive; it is already clear to the Selective Services team examining this problem that *most* of them will be so classified. Methods: (a) will consist of promoting addiction among those in this sub-group who are inherently susceptible; a comparatively small number of agents, we think, will be able to turn a disproportionately large number of terrorists on to hard drugs, at which point they will be dealt with as addicts, as with sub-group 5. (b) is the standard police practice of provocation of political dissidents, whether violence-oriented or not. We will find it more convenient than (a) to use on certain groups that meet *our* criteria, which cooperating police agencies are more likely to accept than in the past as the price for our establishment sanction.

N.B. As you see, most of our operational methods will depend on the cooperation of existing institutions and their personnel. Commission members may find this disturbing. I suggest that when you pass this memo on to them you set a meeting date to discuss it. Ostensibly on means in general, but actually on their misgivings on this point.

Advise—

Arthur

(SHEET containing only the last paragraph of this memo was returned to sender with the following notation: That isn't all they'll find disturbing. You will not only have to explain what has actually been going on for the last few years—they don't know as much as you assume—but you will also have to make it easier for them to visualize how all these rather dramatic procedures can get under way more or less at the same time without leading to acute public indigestion. All your data, definitions, team studies, past experience, practical analyses, operating classifications, and the lot will impress them no end with your analytical competence and your operational judgment, but that's not enough. They must get a better sense of how much the public can swallow at the same time without excessive gagging. You will have to make a few time-space-social ambience pictures—and I don't mean flow charts. In general, I'll handle the social and political projections, but it's still essential for you to demonstrate that you understand them as well as I do. Tomorrow will be it—usual time and place. We're getting down to the bone now, I think, and I think you'll agree with me now, or will tomorrow, that the tax-acceleration caper was absolutely necessary as a starter. *As ever, Frank)*

• THE Commission is now beginning to wrestle seriously with its priorities, criteria, and means. The speed with which Smith and his "Selective Services" have come up with definitions, categories, analyses, and plans—complete with an administrative jargon, which bureaucrats always find necessary as an anaesthetic against the human consequences of abstract schemes—suggests several things.

First, most of the SS work—research and development?—was done before the Commission came into being.

Second, Rooney was familiar with its essential features.

(Whether Smith was the prime mover in getting Rooney to establish the Commission, or whether Rooney sought out Smith's group, is moot: they had been working along parallel lines anyway.)

Third, operational plans for Group One have been developed in much more detail than Smith's chart and explanatory notes indicate. As Rooney's slightly worried response reveals, the function of Smith's memo is to initiate the Commission's members into the more specific realities of what they're getting into.

Fourth, it is probable that Group Two and Three programs are also ready for presentation whenever Rooney thinks the time is right. There is a timetable in the picture somewhere, which has not been disclosed.

THE only one of the "sub-group procedures" that may give pause to Commission members is the seventh, dealing with so-called social terrorists. They don't want to think of themselves as involved with "political" killing, but they will be, despite Smith's casual pragmatism. Yet perhaps he is right to dismiss the distinction, since all programmatic institutional killing is political in a basic sense: it is the exercise of ultimate power.

This is not limited to the narrow context of political assassination. (The recent examples in the United States have been shocking primarily because inconsistent with the premises of democratic process; yet from time immemorial murder has been the political tactic of choice in most societies.) And political genocide is well rooted here. The custom of lynching black people in the south for a century after the civil war and the slaughter of the Indian tribes are the two most conspicuous indigenous models of the use of selective killing to maintain political and economic power: their scale set the pattern for these groups in their relationship to the nation.

These are the relatively obvious examples, along with the police actions that Smith proposes to regulate and authorize. But the

180

other kinds of killing that will be scheduled differ only in degree, and in explicitness, as objectives. The subjugation of one group interest by another—the keep-alives, the unproductive, the inconvenient, etc., versus *us*—also expresses a political conquest.

CHAPTER THIRTEEN

1

Huron City, Nov. 12—Over 600 prisoners and 15 prison guards lay dead today as the worst prison riot in American history ended shortly before dawn.

The carnage ended three violence-filled days as suddenly as it had begun almost exactly 72 hours earlier, when a group of long-term inmates in two maximum-security wings of the state penitentiary here seized the guards as hostages. They had demanded an end to what they called a "deliberate policy of total brutality" allegedly instigated by Warden Elmer Speed, who had taken office only eleven days earlier.

Mr. Speed, who denied the charges, had said at the outbreak of the riot—which had first appeared to be only the latest of an increasing number of violent jailhouse protests intended to publicize prisoners' grievances—that he felt that the real cause of the initial action was the prisoners' resentment at being classified as "habitual criminals" by the new penitentiary administration.

"I have been on record repeatedly," Mr. Speed said, "with my view that the single most self-defeating feature of the prison system has been the indiscriminate intermingling of hardened criminals with potentially redeemable first-offenders and other convicts for whom the possibilities of rehabilitation have not been exhausted. And I wasted no time in separating the two categories here.

"I don't have to tell you how horrified I am at what has happened, but I am still convinced that this was a correct decision. Naturally, I would have moved more slowly if I had had any suspicion what it would lead to. But there were no clues to suggest that a gradual changeover would have gone more smoothly. Our experience indicated quite the contrary."

Although there were no survivors among the prisoners in the two affected sections of the prison, word got through to newsmen and other observers here that the prisoners had claimed that Warden Speed's reclassification of inmates had been accompanied by off-the-record instructions to the guards to crack down on the "habituals" in every possible manner.

One of the guards in the maximum-security wings who was off-duty when the riot started, Thomas Keeling, 39, of Laporte, said that Mr. Speed had told them: "You have to let them know who's boss around here right now, or you'll never be able to."

Mr. Keeling said that he and the other guards had interpreted this to mean that no rule infractions, however minor, were to be tolerated, but he also denied the charge of deliberate brutality.

The question of responsibility for the tragedy was further complicated by confusion about the role of the Department of Justice in the immediate decision to take a "hard line" with the prisoners when the hostages were seized. Mr. Speed said he had been advised—as he put it, "ordered"—to give the prisoners a 48-hour ultimatum to release the captured guards. The ultimatum, he said, was to be unconditional, without even a promise of discussion of grievances.

According to the warden, his questions about the danger to the captured guards were answered by his still-unnamed Washington adviser with a statement to the effect that the risk was one that had to be taken. Unless potentially riotous prisoners throughout the country were finally served "unambiguous notice" that acts of violence directed against prison administrations would be both self-defeating and suicidal, he was told, governmental authorities would lose control of penal institutions.

Also, according to the advice attributed by Mr. Speed to Washington, since such institutions represented the exercise of the maximum authority available to government, loss of control in such situations where the government was assumed to have absolute power would have grave implications for legally constituted authority in general.

Members of the press were not permitted on the penitentiary grounds at any time during the riot and had no first-hand knowledge of what took place or was said over the prison's public address system. However, the sequence of events, amid conflicting reports, appeared to include the following elements:

First, a 48-hour ultimatum was in fact issued at some time during the afternoon of the first day of the riot, November 9. Whether this included a promise to negotiate or discuss grievances later is still unclear.

Second, at the expiration of the 48 hours, a new ultimatum, for an additional six hours, was issued, informing the prisoners that they would now be subject to criminal proceedings for kidnaping regardless of future developments, and that refusal to surrender would lead to an all-out military assault by troops with orders to shoot to kill.

Third, the assault took place, on the night of November 11, and lasted until early morning. How many troops were involved, and what weapons were used, is not yet known, but correspondents who had served in Vietnam believe that the operation must have been modeled on the "no prisoner" extermination assaults developed by U.S. forces in Indo-China.

Neither Mr. Speed nor any other prison or military official was willing to comment at this time on the nature of the assault, nor was any information available on the nature of the prisoners' response to the two ultimata. It appears here that all prison and military personnel involved in the events of the last three days have been instructed to say nothing about them, pending Federal investigation of the circumstances surrounding the riot and its aftermath.

Congressional leaders in Washington, as well as state legislators, have indicated that they do not plan to hold hearings on the matter, as they have been assured by White House sources that the President will appoint a special Board of Inquiry within the next few days.

Names of the convicts killed last night will be released as soon as prison authorities have completed their confirmation of the identities of the bodies, it was announced late this morning. It is expected to take several days. Names and brief biographies of each of the slain guards will be found on the facing page.

2

GILBERT MOSS: We have with us in our studios today Dr. Albert Green, professor of sociology at Delphi College, who is the author of many books in the field of penology. Dr. Green, in your opinion, what questions about the Huron City tragedy should the Federal Board of Inquiry try to answer?

DR. GREEN: First, exactly what really happened. Second, what errors in judgment or policy were responsible. Third, what lessons can be drawn from them to prevent a recurrence. The obvious questions, Mr. Moss.

MR. MOSS: Do you have at this time any theory about policy or tactics that might have been wrong? I'm not asking you to point a finger at any individual.

DR. GREEN: Since the facts of the case are not yet clear, I can hardly be expected to interpret them. However, if the newspaper accounts are correct on certain specifics, there are three questions *I'd* like to see the Board of Inquiry examine closely.

MR. MOSS: Such as?

DR. GREEN: Such as why the 48-hour ultimatum, for one. If true, it's astonishing, absolutely astonishing. Anyone with experience in power situations knows that setting a period appreciably longer than the recipients of an ultimatum *need* to consider it destroys its credibility. Then, to follow *this* with a six-hour choice between prosecution for a possibly capital offense and a defensive pitched battle must have virtually guaranteed the outcome. The prisoners *had* to feel swindled and that they no longer had anything to lose. If the rumors we've all heard about atrocities being committed against the hostages—amputations of ears, tongues and genitals, and so on—turn out to be true, they would have been committed during this period. Many of the convicts were Vietnam veterans, certainly.

MR. MOSS: What would you have done? Would you have given in to the prisoners?

DR. GREEN: Not at all. But the predictable effect of taking a *completely* hard line is to raise the stakes. This is the second question I'd like to see the Board of Inquiry look into. Any military man will tell you that a besieged enemy must be given *some* incentive to surrender, even if only to save face. If you want him to surrender. He has to have a way out, even a bad one, or think he has.

MR. MOSS: You think the guards might have been saved if the convicts had been promised some consideration.

DR. GREEN: I don't know enough of the facts to say for certain, but it would be simple common sense, wouldn't it? Unless, of course, it turns out that some of the convicts had run wild and killed the guards earlier. Now, my third question for the Board is a matter of more general policy. It's been taken too much for granted that habitual criminals should be separated from first offenders and put under maximum discipline. I think this should be restudied. When you have an exclusively hard-core prison population, as you did at Huron City, with no way of expressing grievances or expecting them to be listened to, you get an impossibly virulent atmosphere. Unless you find some way of diluting it, more showdowns like this will be inevitable. The prisons will become more than ever regimes of competing terrors. The hardest convicts will become increasingly desperate and will act accordingly. I'm not optimistic.

3

Washington, Dec. 7—The Department of Health, Education and Welfare today reported a sharp rise in the mortality rate of persons over 65 during the month of November.

According to Dr. George J. Crane, chief of the Bureau of Vital Statistics, the increase, adjusted for seasonal variations, amounted to 11 per cent, as compared to October. It represents, he said, the first statistically significant monthly change in the mortality figures for this age group ever noted, and an unexplained reversal of the long-term trend in the opposite direction.

"We decided to release this information now," he said, "although we are as yet unable to attribute it to any one cause or group of causes. In the past, on those rare occasions when the national death rate has gone up—although never more than slightly—during a particular month, the reason for it has been obvious, such as a major epidemic or an incident of extreme and prolonged air pollution over a large city. In this case, there has been no simple geographical or other factor at hand to explain the rise. It is entirely unprecedented."

Although births and deaths are reported continuously to the Bureau, it normally issues a public report only once a year, usually in March or April of the year following.

Dr. Crane said that the recent short-term increase was "not necessarily disturbing," but that a BVS task force had been set up to analyze the figures exhaustively. "It is possible, of course, that the increase is the result of an extraordinary combination of coincidences," he continued, "but the odds against this are enormous. Yet we have had no great national disasters, no epidemics that were more than local in scope, and no other circumstances at hand that could readily explain a very widely and evenly distributed national phenomenon."

Dr. Crane reported six different types of death that showed unusually high individual increases in November, but said that they had no apparent relationship to each other. "It is not too uncommon for one, or at most two, of these causes to show a significant increase in a particular month," he said, "but not all six." The causes that showed increases were: accidental deaths, up 90 per cent; cancer (all forms), up 18 per cent; cardiovascular diseases, up 10 per cent; hepatitis, up 6 per cent; uremic poisoning, up 5 per cent; and miscellaneous gastro-intestinal infections, up 5 per cent.

"With one obvious exception—accidental deaths—these figures tell us only that these older people died of whatever they were going to die of anyway, only sooner," Dr. Crane explained. "They don't tell us why, which is what we want to find out. The enormous increase in accidental deaths can be accounted for only in minor part by an unusual number of nursing home fires this past month; what we find especially puzzling in this category is why so many more older people, living in all variety of circumstances throughout the country, should have been so unlucky all more or less at once. So far, we have been unable to come up with any plausible common factor, and until we do, we are faced with the choice of two equally unacceptable hypotheses: extraordinary coincidence or some mysterious quasi-pathological factor that transcends our previous experience. However, we'll continue to look."

The BVS chief acknowledged that he and his staff had already begun to engage in preliminary speculation about possible causes, but was reluctant to discuss it. "At the moment every idea we've kicked around seems so far-fetched that we feel rather foolish trying to find ways to test it. For example, is it conceivable that the cumulative effects of polluted air, or of heavy-metal poisoning, have reached the point where they are suddenly showing up in the death rate? Is it possible that some incident, or incidents, of high radioactivity from nuclear testing that took place many years ago is only just now beginning to take its toll? Could it be credible that the deteriorating quality of nursing care could have gone into an extreme and sudden decline? What makes all these minuscule possibilities even more minuscule is the fact that whatever is happening is happening in all parts of the country at the same time. That's the real stumper.

"So far, we're just grabbing at straws. For instance, there has also been a noticeable, in fact a fairly dramatic, increase in deaths due to overdoses of narcotics among *young* people. Could this have any bearing whatever on the increase in the deaths, say from cancer, among people who have had no known association with drugs and are at least two generations older? Common sense says: of course not. But we can't rule out anything yet."

Dr. Crane said that he was going to request the life insurance industry to furnish actuarial and computer assistance to the bureau's task force. "I am confident of their cooperation," he declared, "because they have the biggest financial stake in solving the problem. Until they have some notion of what caused this increase, and whether and to what extent it may continue, they are in real danger."

4

9 Dec
To: All
From: WFR
Re: Today's meeting

Although I promised you no "minutes" for our meetings, I am going to cast this memo approximately in that form, because I think it is important to set down in some degree of organized clarity what went on this morning and who said what. This will also make it easier for me to resist the temptation to tack on my customary useful afterthoughts. You will find it accurate, and I hope helpful. Despite the form, it is still just another of our house memos, to be cast into oblivion after you read it.

Noble Wilson: expressed concern about yesterday's newspaper story from BVS on the increase in over-65 mortality. From his experience in public health, the fact that the BVS actually had its November figures compiled this early, much less that they had begun to analyze them already and that they had issued a public release, indicated that they were more disturbed about this than he had ever known them to be about anything. It wasn't likely to be only a "task force," as Crane said, but the entire resources of the Bureau that would be concentrated on finding an explanation for the mortality rise. It was that important to them, not so much because of its inherent significance but rather because if no plausible reason for the figure could be adduced the whole function of the Bureau would be laid open to question.

Sam Gold: there was no basis for concern about anything BVS might do. From his experience, there was no way BVS could find out that the mortality rise was being programed unless they hypothecated it first, which was inconceivable, and then proved it, which was impossible.

Lew Parker: disagreed. Chiefly, because so many of those involved in executing the program must sense or may even know that what they are doing is part of a national effort; there is bound to be some public speculation of this sort, which not everyone at BVS or elsewhere will necessarily find far-fetched or paranoid.

General discussion. *Consensus:* although the notion that the mortality rise was programed might very well be raised publicly, nothing would come of it. Evidence could not possibly be adduced that would support more than flimsy speculation.

Frank Rooney: first, BVS will work out some hypothesis that will save its face; it doesn't matter what it is, but it won't be the real one, because this is not the kind of answer BVS is geared to consider, even if there were hard evidence. Second, the whole

190

notion that we are engaged in a plot that may be "discovered" or "exposed" is no longer apt. We have a secret, yes, but it is the kind that cannot possibly be "revealed" unless we decide, *collectively,* that it is wise for us to do so. Even if *one* of us were to "psych out," it would carry no credibility unless the rest of us confirmed it. Try to imagine the situation arising, and you'll see what I mean. Third, this kind of "secret" entails wide involvement by people who don't *know* they are part of a centrally controlled plan, but who have a vested interest in silence nevertheless. This is the paradoxical security of the *open* secret, the kind of thing that many people *more or less* know, and is safe for that reason. Think about it. Supposing one or two or a dozen doctors announced that they were killing off certain patients at the suggestion of some mysterious agency. What would the consequences be—if anyone believed it—except to *them?* Too many people are involved.

Which leads to my main point. The *beginning* of public suspicion of what we are doing is good. Suspicion, that is, not revelation. In a fundamental sense, public education is the name of our game. Actually, it has already begun. If we hadn't felt a great subliminal public readiness for extreme measures, a very general sense that our critical social problems were already passing the point of rational solution, we could not, in good faith, and as rational men ourselves, have set out on our giant weeding operation. An important part of what we want to do is to create, through our shock treatment, a more explicit public understanding of how things stand in our world today. If we are sufficiently successful in this, we may even be able to abandon our mission at some point and let the newly educated body politic take over the job. It may be a much less drastic purgative than we are providing, or it may be even more heroic. It doesn't matter. My point, in short, is that we want people to *sense* what we're doing, though not yet exactly how. I would welcome, therefore, some paranoiac charges being made as a result of the BVS statistics.

Prolonged general discussion. General concurrence, but two

demurrers. *Bill Spaatz* and *Henry Harrison:* although the objective sought by Rooney was correct, our lack of control over the events and the publicity that might arise from the BVS story might very well bring down more suspicion than constructive understanding at this time. Urged we should exert what influence we had to play down any charges, and in no case encourage them, as implied by Gold and Rooney.

Bill McGee: any "educational" development of our work was premature. Should not be furthered until our program was so far advanced that any public charge against us would be generally "apprehended" as true. *Compromise:* agreed we would not attempt to influence public discussion that might arise from the BVS story in either direction.

Harrison: the far more dramatic stories of the prison riots and killings last month had apparently prompted no serious suspicion that they were the result of central programing. Perhaps the prison episodes were accepted as a kind of current style in violence, this year's equivalent of the campus shootings and ghetto warfare of a few years back. Also, the well-publicized increase in drug deaths had led to no outcry: both cases may be indicators that public acceptance of institutional killing was under way. Compared the significance of the "non-response" to the famous clue of the dog that *didn't* bark, from Conan Doyle's story.

Rooney (going back to the earlier discussion): should have mentioned that euthanasia, supposedly voluntary but increasingly involuntary, has been practiced by the medical profession much more widely than laymen realize. There has been increasing activity in behalf of legalizing it, in the medical and theological schools, in recent years. *Wilson* confirmed. *Rooney:* one logical response of BVS and other physicians to the new statistics should be that there has probably been a general step-up in euthanasia, leaving them still to consider why now and why so widespread. They *might* reasonably postulate that they are dealing with the execution of an idea whose time has come. They would then logi-

192

cally have to wonder what social catalyst brought it about, since ideas do not reach their time of maturity in a vacuum. If they get this far, they might well speculate that a group like our own could be that catalyst.

None of this negates my previous comments, even though it may seem to. Even if some bolder types find their way to this conclusion, they cannot offer it in behalf of the Bureau as a serious alternative explanation; it is politically unacceptable in their context. A reminder that we are doing just that—acting as a catalyst to a process that has already started. Otherwise we couldn't conceivably get the cooperation from thousands of persons unknown to us, and to whom we are unknown, that makes our operation possible. A reminder that we are in the mainstream of historical necessity, even though well in its vanguard, and that our basic protection lies in this fact. . . . *General assent.*

5

10 Dec
To: All
From: AS
Re: Group Two and Three means.

I will limit myself to general considerations in this memo. You will receive a longer report, detailing proposed procedures schematically, within a few days. Discussion will begin a week from today, per WFR.

Group Two is much less precisely definable than Group One. The chronically unproductive and the generally unemployable are found in all strata of society. Apart from such obvious institutions as retirement communities, certain welfare projects for the handicapped (broadly defined), certain occupations irrevocably committed to nontransferable redundant or nonproductive skills, certain centers of equally irrevocable parasitic life-styles, and a number of old-age and county-home types of institutions not quite qualifying as Group One, the overwhelming majority in Group Two—almost 90 per cent—do not have an institutional locus.

They are best defined geographically. Their prototype, on the scale of what we would today call a pilot project, is the traditional "skid row" still to be found in most big cities. While the population of such concentrated derelict centers has shrunk in recent years, it is not because there is *less* human "waste." On the contrary. It is rather because the progression of our economy has made such a *high* percentage of the population totally disposable, like plastic bottles, that the huge slums of our cities and the multiplying "pockets of poverty" in rural areas have been called into service as human sanitary landfills. Even though they may be no worse physically than they were a generation ago, their function has changed. Whereas they were formerly sources of latent productivity, they are now, functionally, slag piles.

For this reason our procedures must be essentially catastrophic and pandemic. They will involve great fires, explosions, and gassing, as well as floods, earthquakes, and other artificially induced "natural" disasters. They will involve selective pollution of air, water, and foods. They will involve sophisticated techniques of directional radiation, as one kind of example, and of conventional distribution of specially treated foods, toilet articles and the like, as a very different kind.

There is, of course, no way for us to operate on this large a scale without including a high percentage of the potentially productive among the participants. Without going into premature detail, I can report that the criteria we have worked out for the selection of areas will keep this figure below 20 per cent. To get this low a figure, we will have to miss a much higher percentage of those who should be included than we would like. Unless you are prepared to change the criteria to allow the proportion of the improperly eliminated to go well *above* 20 per cent, we will only be able to dispose of about 30 to 35 per cent of those who should be. Efficiency for this group will be low, compared to Group One. But don't confuse the percentages. The 30 to 35 per cent refers to the entire group of eligibles, the 20 per cent is based on those actually disposed of, which means only 6 to 7 per cent of the entire group. Not too bad.

Group Three (social incompetents) presents a different kind of problem. These people have neither geographical, institutional, nor occupational locus. Since their definition is entirely functional, as Frank pointed out in October, they can be dealt with only functionally. The new automobiles will exemplify the means we have to employ with this group, with their useful built-in hazards for those unfit to cope with socially necessary techniques and processes. We propose to extend this principle to electrical and other appliances; to certain kinds of containers, especially those used for foods; to the modification of safety procedures in public transportation systems; to the extension of requirements for sophisticated judgment in the use of self-administered therapeutic drugs; and to a variety of other areas. The principle will be the same as that used in the pollution-free cars. We will develop new and advantageous technological improvements—in most cases this means only that we will stimulate the distribution of new products and systems that have already been worked out—that will have in common a low tolerance for error in their use, whether because of their complexity or their precision. In general, errors in their use will tend to be fatal. They will be programed to endanger only those whose incompetence is of the kind that constitutes a constant danger and expense for society as a whole.

Another area in which we expect to work—one implied by my mention of public transportation systems—is in the elimination of conventional safety devices that drain the general economy. There is no reason, for example, why the great majority of competent and rational automobile drivers should have to underwrite enormously expensive traffic control systems geared to the lowest level of irresponsibles. We will offer some interesting proposals in this area. In

195

general, however, our Group Three programs will evolve quite gradually and naturally, as we see it, and the results will not begin to appear on the statistical tables for some time. . . .

• THE Special Commission on National Priorities has been in existence only ten weeks. Elimination of Group One "participants" is well under way. Procedures for dealing with Groups Two and Three will soon be codified. It is obvious that the Commission's scale of operations will continue to expand rapidly.

There has been much discussion, especially by Rooney, of the factors affecting public acceptance of the killings. Another contributory element may be worth noting, itself a product of the same social psychopathology. It is the widespread feeling of undifferentiated, amorphous threat; of vulnerability to a hostile environment; of exposure to an implacable, violent retribution in redress of unknown and unarticulated grievances. These unfocused social fears are assuaged by catastrophe—by assurance that the great faceless enemy is equally vulnerable, that other unknown forces can neutralize his menace. Which is to say that disaster can be comforting for its survivors.

PART FOUR

CHAPTER FOURTEEN

THIS account will now move ahead five months, to the following
May.

A great deal has happened during this period, all of which has
conspired to make staying alive an increasingly chancy business for
persons unfortunate enough to be scheduled for "participation" in
the Commission's program. For some of its categories, survival has
become a minority privilege. The catastrophes, epidemics, and
other means proposed by Selective Services (and ratified by the
Commission sooner or later) have been actuated on a large scale
more or less according to plan, with few changes. "Implementation" has proceeded without delay. Here are the observable results,
so far.

1. *A continuing increase in the mortality rate of older persons.* If Dr.
Crane and his staff have come to any conclusions about the phenomenon, they have kept quiet about it. This has not been difficult,
because these deaths have been comparatively undramatic, in the
context of other events. The BVS actuaries in the task force investigation have determined a few things:

> . . . the increase in deaths took place almost exclusively
> among those with already poor life expectancy. . . .

Although a disproportionately high share [took place in] institutions committed to the care of functionally terminal cases, no statistical difference was noted between deaths in cancer wards and intensive care units of major teaching hospitals, at one extreme, and poorly equipped rural homes for the aged and indigent, at the other. . . .

Those deaths classified as accidental resulted primarily from medical and custodial errors, including incorrect assignment of drugs, carelessness of paramedical personnel, poor food handling, and failure of building equipment and maintenance. . . .

They also noted a small but rising offsetting trend—a higher percentage of recoveries among younger hospital patients classified as "critical," which they have tentatively attributed to the greater availability of hospital beds and services resulting from the higher death rate among the old. (But in certain cities this trend has been itself offset in turn by a shortage of nurses.)

2. *Numerous outbreaks of serious epidemics.* All have been local, limited to institutions or small areas. This may explain the otherwise surprising paucity of national publicity, despite the fact that total casualties have already exceeded those of the great epidemics following World War I. In the only network television interview dealing with the phenomenon, the Surgeon-General said:

. . . I see no cause for alarm, Mr. Crocker. This is not one of the classic plagues, but a multiplicity of local situations, which must be dealt with locally. You may call it an epidemic of epidemics, if you like the phrase, but they don't have enough in common to be discussed as an entity.

. . . Sources? The usual. Bad water supply, contaminated foods, and so on. . . . Yes, there have been some special problems. One is the recent proliferation of new strains of drug-resistant bacteria. Another is the problem of getting uncontaminated blood plasma. . . . Probably because in this country plasmapheresis stations are run like businesses.

When we enforce strict quality controls, the supply goes to hell. . . .

. . . Well, naturally, most of the outbreaks take place in "closed" institutions, like prisons and hospitals. But they do affect certain *types* of communities as well. . . . Where sanitary practices tend to be inadequate. Mostly urban slums, or isolated rural areas, like the typhus last month in Alabama. . . . No, it's not limited to the South or any other region. It might be easier to deal with if it were.

3. *A spectacular increase in the deaths of drug addicts and the beginning of a sharp decline in visible addiction.* Overdosing has been the proximate cause of by far the largest number of these deaths, which have been fairly well reported. From a New York morning daily:

. . . No single explanation can adequately account for it, Dr. White said, but at least three of the many theories advanced are known to have substance. The most obvious, he indicated, was the wide and apparently uncontrollable variation in the purity of heroin supplies; another was the apparent growing reduction in tolerance to drugs. The third factor, he said, was the escalation of the addicts' presumed "death wish," believed by many psychiatrists to motivate drug-taking.

A more puzzling aspect of the drug deaths, on which Dr. White would not comment, has been that the fatality rate for users of neomorph and methadone (participants in withdrawal programs) has been just as high as that of the general addict population.

All the experts interviewed agreed that the decline in addiction has been most dramatic in New York City, which is now far behind other major cities in per capita drug consumption. New York is now believed to rank no higher than third in total drug usage, trailing well behind Los Angeles and Houston. . . .

These deaths have given rise to no public concern, except among the families of those directly affected. It may be assumed that they have led to an unexpressed sense of relief at the diminution of drug addiction as social and criminal problem.

4. *The resurgence of gang warfare among criminals.* It has been more sophisticated and more certain than its Chicago-1920s prototype—very little shooting, no cement-clad bodies dumped in lakes and rivers. From a TV discussion transcript:

MR. CROCKER: If 75 per cent of the mobsters you indict are murdered before they come to trial, wouldn't you say that an indictment is now a virtual death sentence?

ATTORNEY-GENERAL MARTIN: It is a problem. We try to protect them, of course, but they are often killed before the indictment is announced or the papers served. There are leaks.

MR. HARTLEY: What effect does this have on your decisions to prosecute or not prosecute?

MR. MARTIN: I have instructed all U.S. attorneys to be absolutely sure of their cases before seeking indictments and to make sure the offenses are sufficiently serious.

MR. HARTLEY: You mean murder or the equivalent? I've been told quite the opposite. I'm told some D.A.s and grand juries are going after indictments now that they *know* wouldn't stand a chance of conviction. They're inviting the mobs to kill the accused.

MR. MARTIN: That's a slander, Mr. Hartley. It's possible that some local state or county attorneys may be less conscientious than they should be, but the Department of Justice will not condone such carelessness by any U.S. attorney's office.

MR. HARTLEY: That's not what we see, Mr. Martin. I should think that in good faith you should guarantee protection to anyone for whom an indictment is being sought.

MR. MARTIN: It's a physical impossibility.

MR. MOSS: Well, if you're sure you have the goods on them it's a hell of a cheap way to break up the mobs. I can understand the temptation.

MR. CROCKER: But how can you ever be so sure? And why do the mobs seem to expect their people to talk nowadays if they're indicted? They used to trust each other and enforce their own arrangements, didn't they?

MR. MARTIN: Well, we don't know who's in charge any more, that's true.

5. *The open establishment of killer vigilante groups in large cities.* These groups have publicized and documented their activities, anonymously, so that earlier doubts of their actual existence have been dispelled. For example, they have left the same "calling card" at the scene of each execution, a sword wrapped in an American flag. From the identity of the victims and from the quality of the information that must have been at their disposal, it is clear that they have had the cooperation of high police officials. Most of their members are themselves police. They have had a mixed press. From a Chicago editorial:

> . . . In no way do we defend or accept the outrageous assumption of extra-legal power by these self-styled protectors of public safety. But we must at the same time acknowledge that public approval of their activities, as confirmed by a recent poll, is based on a certain folk wisdom that no thinking person can safely ignore. The fact is—and we remind our readers of it only as a fact and not as a justification —that these high-handed killers *have* reduced crime in our cities, just as did their predecessors in the 19th-century "Wild West."
> But their more responsible leaders must take note that the public support they currently enjoy will quickly fall away if

they presume to pass judgment on what they call "political" criminals. We hope that the disquieting recent example in Detroit does not mark the beginning of a new phase in which their indisputable success in thinning out the ranks of obvious criminal elements is extended to presumptions of political authority. In this direction lies the police state. We appeal to the sense of justice that inspired their enterprise, however mistakenly conceived, to bring these activities to an end while they may still claim, in good conscience, a measure of public gratitude. . . .

None of these comments, we repeat, should be construed as even a qualified endorsement of these killings. They make a mockery of a society based on law. Our democratic way of life will not permit . . .

6. *Political warfare.* From a dispatch to *Le Monde,* Paris:

. . . The Oakland confrontation, which resembled a small-scale formal military engagement, expresses the great new fact of American political violence: it has turned inward. More often than not, as in this case, the antagonists are conflicting radical factions, usually within the same political movement.

Why this is so is not entirely clear, although it is evident that police agents have been active on a much greater scale than heretofore. Until recently, the greatest physical hazard of radical politics here has been the "shoot-out" deliberately provoked by police. But it now appears that the police have succeeded in stimulating spontaneous warfare among radicals without participating openly themselves.

Right-wing paramilitary groups, of the Minuteman and Klan types, continue as before to take violent action against leftists and third-world groups of all persuasions, with no perceptible discouragement from local or federal law-enforcement bureaus. But today these "putsch" type maneuvers are far less significant than the suicidal and fratricidal activities of the left groups themselves.

One must ask, as always: *cui bono?* It is too soon to offer a definitive answer, but it is abundantly clear that radical and liberal activities formerly directed against the military and industrial power complexes have been effectively paralyzed. . . .

7. *Military accidents.* The moving of stockpiles of poison gas, live ammunition, bacteria, and nuclear devices has been attended by an unprecedented number of unexplained accidents, resulting in high mortality among communities affected. (Included here are three instances of non-military shipments of vinyl chlorine, which gives off phosgene, a gas used in chemical warfare, when heated.) One reason they are unexplained is that the Department of Defense has been successful in keeping many of the incidents secret. From a D.o.D. not-for-attribution briefing in a case that could not be concealed:

MR. CLARK: The Secretary has instructed me to tell you that the Department cannot accept responsibility for what happened at Memphis, since the shipment was not under our effective jurisdiction. However, the Department intends to put every facility at its command to clean up the areas affected and to assist the survivors of this terrible tragedy.

REPORTER: But the gas was en route to the Aberdeen testing grounds, wasn't it? How can you say you had no jurisdiction?

MR. CLARK: We had not taken title to the material. I must stand on the previous statement.

REPORTER: Nearly five hundred people were killed. Are you saying that the Department is cleaning up the area only from the goodness of its heart?

MR. CLARK: I refer you to the previous statement. However, I am happy to add that the victims did not include any military personnel, or others essential to national security.

205

REPORTER: But the responsibility was entirely that of the shipper?

MR. CLARK: Or of the carrier. That is correct.

8. *Twelve catastrophic fires, killing a total of some 22,000 persons and making another 200,000 homeless.* These, of course, did hit the headlines, and in so doing reduced the attention that might otherwise have been focused on some of the other phenomena reported here. All took place in urban slums, except for one brush fire near Los Angeles. Their causes have not been definitely established; in most cases they are believed to have been started, as is common in cold weather, from defective heating equipment. However, what transformed them from statistically predictable incidents of the season into holocausts was the common factor in inadequate response by fire departments. Invariably, by the time fire-fighting equipment arrived on the scene the fire was already out of control.

Why? The reasons varied. Either the firemen had been dispersed in other parts of the cities by false alarms (as in Philadelphia), or had mistaken the calls from the burning buildings as false alarms in the first place (as in Dallas), or had been on strike (in three instances), or had been effectively delayed by hostile residents of the neighborhoods (as in New York), or had been prevented from reaching the scene or from getting water on the blaze by malfunctioning trucks or pumps, presumably sabotaged (as in Chicago and Cleveland). No evidence remains to substantiate arson.

The false-alarm rate had already become so high by the time the first of these great fires took place, in late January, that all fire-fighting had long since become chronically demoralized. In many localities, equipment is no longer sent out in response to an alarm until a member of the fire company goes out personally to confirm the existence of an actual fire. But usually this doesn't work either, since the false-alarm rate often keeps all firemen busy on confirmation duty. In addition, the incidence of fires known to have been set by arsonists had also become so high that what happened in the twelve great conflagrations surprised no one.

9. *Four episodes of killing smog.* Each involved a permanently depressed coal town, a severe condition of temperature inversion, and a mixture of noxious gases, very much like the classic Donora case in 1948. What was unusual is that only one of the four towns was believed to have had any potential air pollution problem at all; the others were comparatively clean, in terms of automobile exhausts, heating plants, and industrial by-products. Meteorologists have not yet been able to account for them. Nevertheless: about 4,500 killed, all four towns abandoned.

10. *A major subway disaster in New York.*

> ... The initial collapse appeared to have taken place near the Hunts Point station in the East Bronx at 4:38 P.M. An apparent chain reaction followed almost immediately, extending the area of destruction to about half a mile along the Pelham line of the IRT. ... The sequence of events is believed to have been: collision, fire, explosion, collapse of the street immediately above, further collapse and fire. ... Preliminary estimates put the number of dead at about 800 and the seriously injured at about 2,300. Police, fire, and transit officials admitted, however, that these figures may prove to be low. ... Almost all the victims were believed to have been residents of the immediate area of the disaster, parts of which have often been described as a "slum jungle."

11. *The great welfare food scandal.* It was discovered, almost by accident, that much of the food distributed under surplus-food plans, consumed chiefly by persons on relief, was contaminated to a lethal degree. Although all the figures are not yet in, the mortality has been moderate (probably under a thousand nationally). But

this low figure is entirely fortuitous. It is hard to say how many hundreds of thousands owe their lives to a young doctor in Eastern Kentucky who became suspicious of the origins of seemingly unrelated illnesses and fatalities among his welfare patients. Amoebic dysentery, typhus, botulism, and a variety of more exotic ailments appeared in puzzling circumstances; only because of one man's bullheadedness was the common factor determined and the foods embargoed.

No one has yet come up with a tenable explanation of how and why not one but many of the surplus foods were contaminated—rice, beans, potatoes, and certain canned meats. The foods in question have been ordered destroyed; nevertheless, reports of similar "nutrition problems" in Asia, Latin America, and Africa have begun to trickle in. A Congressional investigation has been started.

12. *Water trouble.* Apart from the epidemics previously mentioned that started from contaminated water supply, the last several months have seen a surprising number of instances of simple poisoning spread through water systems. The poisons have varied —mercury salts, lead compounds, arsenic, pesticides—with no solutions recorded despite a veritable pharmacopeia of suspicions. Although most of the water systems affected have served depressed areas, one of the most virulent cases took place in a wealthy retirement community in Arizona. Pollution experts and hydraulic engineers are working on the problem.

13. *Free samples.* A number of small communities and urban neighborhoods have been decimated by poisoners distributing "introductory" free samples of merchandise. As a rule, they have carried the labels of well-known manufacturers, and have been left at the doorsteps of residents of urban and rural slums along with flyers notifying the recipients of their good fortune in being part of a test-marketing program. From the national warning issued by the Bureau of Consumer Fraud:

. . . Do not accept, if possible do not touch, and above all *do not taste* these items. Most reputable food and drug manufacturers have agreed to discontinue this kind of market testing until the danger has passed. This warning applies especially, but it not limited to *toothpastes, breakfast foods,* and *mouthwashes. . . .*

. . . Do not permit any self-styled "furnace adjuster" not known to you *to have access to your stove or furnace.* Accept no "free inspection" offer. In the event the complexion of any member of your household should take on an unfamiliar "cherry-red" cast not clearly accounted for, check with your doctor or nearest clinic to rule out carbon monoxide poisoning. . . .

. . . In some cases, *hair tonics, detergents, soaps,* and even *magazines* have been distributed in this manner that have been impregnated with a new poison developed by the Department of Defense that may kill on sufficient contact. Dispose of such items immediately, *wearing rubber gloves.* Then soak the gloves thoroughly in *vinegar* before again touching the parts of the gloves which have been in contact with the suspected items. . . .

No promising clues to the sources of the poisonings have yet turned up. The principal investigation is being made under Army auspices, its purpose being to find out how CBW security procedures have been circumvented, rather than to determine the causes and logistics of the killings. However, the bizarre hoax, a kind of metastasized version of the occasional psychotic Halloween candy poisoner, appears to be tapering off.

14.   *Air crashes.* From the preliminary examiners' report to the Federal Aviation Administration:

. . . We have as yet been unable to determine any operational factors common to the fatal accidents that have taken place since 1 March, other than that all sixteen aircraft were chartered by physically handicapped groups, (mentally ill, aged, and retarded; we also include here two military aircraft carrying critical battlefield casualties). This does not appear relevant to a determination of cause of failure. No relating patterns of pilot error, improper maintenance, or possible insurance fraud have yet emerged. . . .

. . . Airline patrons may take some reassurance, however, from the fact that none of the crashes involved a regularly scheduled passenger flight. . . .

15. *Natural disasters.* That the last three months should have seen a great flood in northeastern Brazil, an unseasonal typhoon in India, and a major earthquake in the Rift Valley of central Africa can hardly be laid to the machinations of the Special Commission. However, the unbelievable sluggishness of relief operations, noted repeatedly by emergency conferences of the World Health Organization in Geneva, may be something else again. It may have had its prototype in the "rescue" operations of the Pakistan government in the great flood of 1970; even before the East Bengal massacres, it was hard to believe that such inefficiency could have been the result of mere incompetence. That the United States military, then in full force in southeast Asia, sent only *four* helicopters to pick up survivors raises the question that Smith's people may have been practicing "Group Four" operations long before the Special Commission was organized.

• WHAT has been the public reaction to these developments? The private response? One might expect the accelerated disappearance of so many from the ranks of the living to provoke some sort of crisis. Like other complex organisms, a social system can adapt only to relatively minor variations in its component processes. The "normal" death rate has more than doubled during this period, and with a highly selective emphasis; this is no minor variation.

The answer is: not so much. (A surprisingly high proportion of the victims were not even missed.) The more dramatic episodes made newspaper headlines, to be sure. But headlines are printed every day, and are part of the conditioned daily intake of those who have learned to expect routine communication of "news," on a front page of the same size or on a television program of the same length, regardless of contents. The sameness tends to level its impact. That suddenly the news begins to consist preponderantly of stories of death and disaster does not change its character as "news" in proportion to its substance.

But paradoxically, the cumulative effect on social behavior of the changing contents of announced news builds up rapidly. A large element of fear, of procedures of ordinary life that only yesterday were taken for granted as secure, has now become quickly assimilated into the normal mode of getting through the day. The old phrase "when your number comes up" has acquired new meaning. Just as big-city residents long ago became accustomed, when returning home late at night, to reconnoitering their doorways like paratroopers on point, so have people now become equally wary of other segments of their daily routines. They may not yet be turning into assassins themselves, as some have suggested, but they are already behaving as if they thought their neighbors were. They are right, to a degree; *conventional* homicides are also becoming increasingly common, as day-to-day living continues on its course of devaluation, like a currency going soft.

People tend to do what they *assume* is expected of them—however unacceptable their actions may appear, even to themselves, at sufficient distance in time. And they readily learn to accept—as normal—the actions of others that can be justified only by assigning prime value to adaptation to things as they are *assumed* to be. How else can one explain the lack of lasting response to the endless catalogue of human atrocities? The daily casualty

211

lists from battlefields and the counts of "enemy" dead are taken to be part of a *natural* order of things, however much deplored, opposed, protested, or resisted. As indeed have been all the great genocides of our times—in the German concentration camps; in the World War II bombings; in Indonesia, Nigeria, Pakistan, Indo-China, anywhere—sooner or later, whatever the rhetoric, however genuine the revulsion. Facts of life, facts of history.

So it has been with the new wave of killings and unexplained deaths. Of course there has been public concern. Of course there have been recriminations. There have been episodes of panic, among groups and communities most directly affected by the activities of the Special Commission. And there has been unease, and even occasional hysteria, among individuals who sense that malevolent social forces may be at work and directed against *them*. For the ordinary person—buffeted about at the mercy of vast unseen social processes that he cannot recognize, much less comprehend—it has never been easy to distinguish clearly between paranoia and prudence. But now it is becoming very hard indeed.

The fact that the killings have been widely dispersed in place, in time, and especially in form has made it impossible for those truly in danger to protect themselves. There can be no effective defense against the killings until they are understood—and until a counter-strategy, based on that understanding, is organized. This may not happen. One of the premises that brought the Special Commission into being is that the body politic will not recognize its own impending breakdown or act upon the necessities of that recognition until the damage is past the point of no return. The premise may be wrong, but so far there is no evidence of it.

THE Commission has taken upon itself to decide who shall live and who shall die, thus asserting the ultimate political power—to kill with impunity. This power has always been the basis of authority, whether of a barbarian chief or in a modern constitutional state, where it has been disguised and refined to appear compatible with declared humanitarian values. The Commission has only exercised it more candidly than have those social and economic institutions that foreshorten the lives of masses of people in less conspicuous ways.

In successful social systems, the effective regimentation of those who do the dirty work has always required the weeding out of those who interfere with the productivity of the useful. The prevailing mode calls for casting the culls into prisons, terminal institutions, or subsistence communities, burying them alive as cheaply as possible. But it is still cheaper to bury them dead, and this has always been the treatment of choice when the percentage of rejects is as high, and as potentially unmanageable, as the Special Commission thinks it has become.

The Commission has justified its decisions as social necessity— the greater good. But exercising the power to put them into effect implies an inherent self-interest; the claim to moral objectivity is inevitably compromised. It may not matter; it may be argued that social "morality" must be a reflection of macro-biological processes beyond our comprehension or control, and that any constructed moral system may thus be irrelevant to our survival. To accept such a notion, however, would be to abandon hope of achieving any measure of management over the quality of our lives; this would defy not merely blind faith but the judgment of common experience. So some principle of social morality may still be in order. Perhaps, to begin with, respect for the sanctity of human life? If so, how can it be sustained so long as men and their institutions stand to profit from the death of others?

CHAPTER FIFTEEN

1

Washington, Oct. 1—The President's Special Commission on National Priorities observed the anniversary of its first meeting quietly today, amid rumors that it was about to issue a report calling for drastic reordering of national goals.

Although Commission Chairman William Francis Rooney refused to comment directly on the rumors, he indicated in an informal session with a selected group of media representatives here that he expected to present the President and the general public with a "record of achievement" along with certain specific programmatic recommendations. He dismissed queries about the nature of the achievement referred to, other than to say that the recent dramatic improvement in economic and other "indices of social health" would be dealt with in detail at a general news conference to be scheduled concurrent with the presentation of the report "some time in November," presumably after the elections.

In response to a question about the surprising lack of overt Congressional criticism of the Commission's "invisibility," Dr. Rooney said that he had made it a matter of his own "personal priority" to keep Congressional and Executive branch leaders informed of the group's progress and activities, "on a man-to-man basis." "It seems to have worked," he declared with a smile. "I learned not too long ago that if I keep a supply of bones and dog biscuits on hand I don't get

214

bitten." He was referring to his earlier experience as a Presidential adviser, which had been punctuated by continual controversy with legislators and administrators.

Ridiculing charges of excessive secrecy brought by two reporters against the Commission's closed-door proceedings, Dr. Rooney said that although he would not be provoked into "premature and untimely" disclosures, he could and would guarantee his interrogators "more candor than you'll know what to do with" at the November conference.

Dr. Rooney recently returned from London, where he had conferred with top-level priorities groups similar to his that had been organized in the United Kingdom, France, and West Germany. He described the outlook for "effective cooperation" between the four countries as "excellent," and expressed confidence that unnamed other nations, including, he implied, some in the Soviet and Chinese blocs, would also involve themselves in a program of mutual consultation.